Energy and environmental issues for the practising architect:
a guide to help at the initial design stage

Ian C. Ward

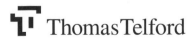
Thomas Telford

Published by Thomas Telford Publishing, Thomas Telford Ltd, 1 Heron Quay, London E14 4JD.
www.thomastelford.com

Distributors for Thomas Telford books are
USA: ASCE Press, 1801 Alexander Bell Drive, Reston, VA 20191-4400, USA
Japan: Maruzen Co. Ltd, Book Department, 3–10 Nihonbashi 2-chome, Chuo-ku, Tokyo 103
Australia: DA Books and Journals, 648 Whitehorse Road, Mitcham 3132, Victoria

First published 2004

A catalogue record for this book is available from the British Library

ISBN: 0 7277 3216 1

© Thomas Telford Limited 2004

Typeset by Academic + Technical, Bristol
Printed and bound in Great Britain by MPG Books, Bodmin

Contents

Contents

Introduction

Background

This book is intended to help the everyday designer understand the issues involved in producing energy efficient and sustainable building design. It is intended to be used on everyday designs where there are likely to be restrictions either related to the design parameters themselves or on the financial commitment of the client.

Section 1 — The need to conserve energy

This section deals with why it is important to consider energy and sustainability in design work. It starts with an outline of the work of the International Panel on Climate Change highlighting the fact that the energy consumed by buildings is contributing to global warming. It concludes with an outline of the many issues which are important when considering sustainable building design.

Section 2 — Basic information about energy use in buildings

Before energy and sustainability issues can be applied to a building design it is necessary to have a broad understanding of the various issues at play and a little about the technicalities involved. This section deals with the following:

1. Points in the RIBA plan of work when energy issues are important
2. Occupant comfort

◆ Metabolic rate of humans
◆ Factors affecting heat gains/losses from the human body

- Air temperature effects
- Humidity effects
- Air movement around the human
- Air quality
- Lighting
- Glare
- Environmental noise
- Internal heat gains

3. Building design issues

- Plan form
- Window design
- Thermal insulation
- U values
- Thermal mass
- Mechanical services
- Ventilation systems
- Heat recovery systems
- Lighting systems.

Section 3 — Aids at design stage to help produce an energy efficient building

This section covers the simple methods which can be used to help to produce an efficient building design for energy efficiency and space for the mechanical services. Areas covered are:

- Site analysis
- Building form
- Thermal insulation
- Estimation of thermal mass
- Plant room space
- Distribution space.

Section 4 — How to deal with environmental factors at the design stage

An outline of the various elements which must be considered at the design stage is given in a simplified way along with a method of demonstrating the effectiveness of a design in sustainability terms.

Section 5 — Some case studies of mainstream buildings which are energy or environmentally efficient

Several case studies are presented in such a way as to illustrate how energy and sustainability can be incorporated into normal commercially accepted design. The examples are taken from buildings in the UK, Germany, France and Switzerland. The case studies are:

- Dearne Valley College, Barnsley, UK
- Commercial Offices ECO Centre, Jarrow, UK
- Commercial Offices for BT, Coventry, UK
- Private House, Wirksworth, Derbyshire, UK
- Concept industrial and distribution centre, Milton Keynes, UK
- Notley Green Primary School, Essex, UK
- Offices, Chur, Switzerland
- Housing in Stäfa, Switzerland
- Housing balance project in Uster, Switzerland
- Kindergarten in Stuttgart, Germany
- Leonardo da Vinci Secondary School, Calais, France.

Bibliography

Selected references and sources.

Section 1

The need to conserve energy

Introduction

The energy and environmental efficiency of our buildings is perhaps the most important aspect of design facing the profession for the next several years. For some time now it has been recognised that the mean surface temperature of the Earth has been increasing and many scientists believe that this is the result of the increasing emission of what has become known as 'greenhouse gases'. To investigate the extent of this problem a panel of internationally recognised scientists known as the Intergovernmental Panel on Climate Change (IPCC) has been given the task of establishing if this increase in temperature is linked to these emissions and to suggest ways in which the international community can deal with this problem in light of the rapid development of industrial nations.

The popular phrase Global Warming is now recognised as one of the driving forces for climate change. Figure 1.1 taken from the IPCC document illustrates quite clearly the rapid increase in mean surface temperature over the past 100 or so years. Leading on from this the IPCC has also produced evidence of significant human activity which is causing an increase in the concentration of certain gases in the atmosphere. Figure 1.2 illustrates quite clearly that the effect of the industrialisation of the globe is having a significant effect on the concentration of these gases.

Coupled with this there have been several meetings of governments, starting with the Rio de Janeiro Convention in the early 1990s, at which international agreements on the control of these harmful emissions were discussed and countries encouraged to adopt measures to reduce these emissions. Since then there have been further meetings at which agreements on climate change issues ranging from deforestation through sustainable development to the use of renewable energy have been agreed by many countries.

Currently the UK is committed to reducing its greenhouse gas emissions by 14% from those produced in 1990 and in the UK

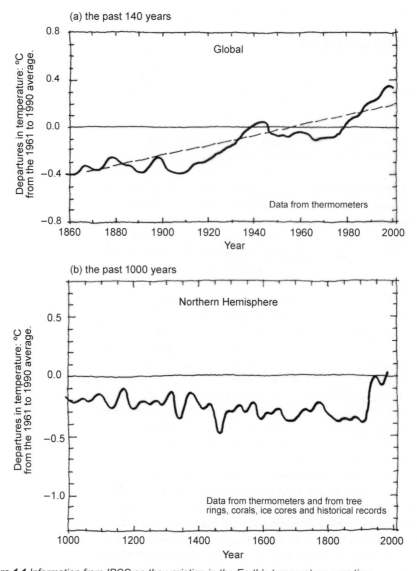

Figure 1.1 *Information from IPCC on the variation in the Earth's temperature over time*

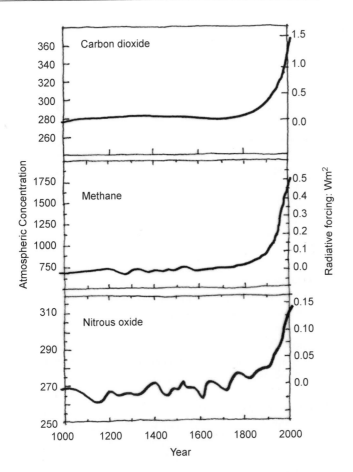

Figure 1.2
*Indicators of human
influence on the
atmosphere – IPCC*

Government's White Paper on Energy there is an aspiration that by
2050 our carbon emissions will be reduced by 60%. In one of the
IPCC's reports it identifies buildings as being one of the main
contributors to global warming, being responsible for the use of nearly
24% of the energy used globally in 1990 with an annual growth rate of
1%, which puts further pressure on the designers and operators of
buildings to ensure that their designs are as energy and
environmentally friendly as possible. To achieve this level of
reduction will inevitably mean significant changes in lifestyle and in
the design and operation of our buildings.

Table 1.1. *The variation in energy consumption by sector and the percentage of that energy used to heat, cool and ventilate the building*

	GJ/m²/yr	Percentage used to heat, light, cool and ventilate
Commercial offices	0.9	84
Communication and transport	0.47	76
Education	0.87	75
Government (excluding defence)	1.1	78
Health	1.7	83
Hotel and catering	1.6	54
Other	1.0	81
Retail	1.1	70
Sport and leisure	0.8	51
Warehouses	0.7	76

In the UK almost half of the energy used is for the operation of our buildings (providing heat, cooling, ventilation and electrical power for equipment), which again emphasises the fact that buildings are important in the drive to reduce both national and global consumption of resources. Even within the building sector there is a wide range of energy uses, as Table 1.1 demonstrates, and therefore it is important to assess at an early stage in the process the likely impact the project will have on energy requirements. For example, there is little benefit from spending too much design time on a storage facility where the heating energy is minimal, whereas a sports centre or health care building will have greater consumptions and therefore are likely to benefit more from a closer analysis of the design in terms of energy usage.

To this end several measures have been adopted by government to ensure that these targets are met. Given that in the UK we are replacing our building stock at a rate of about 1% per year and on average commercial buildings are refurbished every five years there is an onus on designers and operators of buildings to ensure that the designs and service systems are as energy efficient and environmentally sustainable as possible. It is now no longer the case that we can only play at dealing with these issues: clients and regulations are pushing designers to take these issues seriously.

How do we start?

It has been stated that to produce a building which uses energy and environmental resources efficiently, it is essential that the requirements of the occupants be considered along with the detail design of the fabric, services systems and operational energy use. Of equal importance is the ability of the products of use (waste paper for example) and the materials used to produce the building can be recycled, reused or efficiently disposed of at the end of their useful life.

This is a minefield and often seen by designers to be too difficult or too time consuming to investigate these issues. However, it need not be the case since, as in most things, by keeping things simple and dealing with the issues one at a time we can often arrive at a reasonable solution. To be able to integrate these requirements it is first necessary to have a broad understanding of which ones are of importance, their effects and limits.

At the beginning of a design dialogue between the client and the architect, the requirements of the client are explored before a concept design is produced. At this stage if some of the energy/environmental issues are explored, quite often they can be incorporated quite simply and will result in the building being more efficient in both energy and environmental terms.

The following brief descriptions of some of the more important aspects in energy and environmental design are intended to illustrate the wide range of issues which need to be addressed early on in the design process. These descriptions are not intended to be a rigorous explanation of all their aspects, however. Their application will be expanded upon in subsequent sections and illustrated through rule-of-thumb techniques or case studies of buildings incorporating some or all of these features.

Occupant comfort

One of the issues of importance to both parties is the internal environmental comfort of the occupants and there is still a belief that we should be designing our buildings to have internal air temperatures of between 20°C and 23°C. To do so often places great strain on both the architect and the services designers to adhere to these requirements. By adopting a more flexible approach to comfort within spaces it is often the case that expensive air conditioning or excessive mechanical ventilation can be avoided or at least minimised.

In all thermal comfort studies it is recognised that the clothing levels of the occupants plays a significant role in the sensation of thermal comfort. Many of the studies carried out were done when the dress code was more rigorous than is perhaps the norm today. Men were usually regarded as wearing suits with ties and women similarly attired (perhaps not with ties). Today in the less formal workplace the dress of both sexes tends to have less thermal insulation properties and therefore both sexes are tending to be more susceptible to draughts and fluctuating temperatures. The seating position within the space can also affect the sensation of thermal comfort. For example, a person wearing a lightweight shirt (or blouse), lightweight trousers (or skirt) seated near an open window is more likely to complain of thermal discomfort (even if the air temperature is in the low twenties) than a person seated in the middle of the space. This spread of comfort across internal spaces has been reported many times in thermal comfort analysis studies.

Increasingly designers are realising that occupants of buildings are able to tolerate a wider range in comfort conditions than those specified in the Chartered Institute of Building Services Engineers Handbook. This is a result of a better understanding of the psychology of how people react to their environment. For example, if the outside temperature is in the upper twenties on a sunny day then occupants will tolerate temperatures in the mid twenties within their office environment provided other aspects of comfort such as air movement and humidity are also considered. This type of comfort analysis is generally referred to as adaptive thermal comfort.

Temperature

The British Council of Offices has adopted this work in its specification of temperatures for office spaces. Generally in well-designed office environments internal temperatures in the region of 23°C to 25°C are regarded as being acceptable in summer. In winter it is recommended that an internal air temperature of 18°C is aimed for; however, in general practice 20°C to 22°C is often found. These conditions, although set for office environments, are also quite acceptable in other situations, and particularly in buildings where the occupancy is transient – for example moving through a shopping centre, watching a race in a swimming pool and many other situations.

Humidity

The humidity of the air within a space is generally not regarded as being very important. People are able to tolerate a wider range in humidity than air temperature and in the vast majority of internal spaces the humidity usually ranges from about the mid thirties to the upper sixties. The vast majority of occupants are quite able to tolerate this range. However, if the humidity is in the upper sixties along with high air temperatures and no or very little air movement then the three measures combined may give rise to a larger proportion of the occupants feeling uncomfortable.

Air movement

Air movement within an environment is required to remove heat and to provide fresh air to the space. It is always a problem to design a system which will carry this out efficiently under all operating conditions. The general design specifications for air movement are that the air speed should not be above about 1.5 m/s around the body.

Carbon dioxide levels

Increasingly the concentration of carbon dioxide in internal environments is being taken into consideration. High carbon dioxide levels have been shown to be a major cause of people feeling tired or lethargic. By ensuring that these levels are kept low, the internal atmosphere is regarded as being fresh. Accepted values above which action should be taken are in the region of 800–1000 ppm.

Lighting

Lighting is extremely important and it is essential that it is considered in detail at the design stage. People are able to perform visual tasks more efficiently if they have good quality lighting and in the working and leisure environments of today it is also essential to consider the lighting of computer screens. In the majority of internal environments a lighting level of at least 300–400 lux on the working plane will normally be satisfactory, although with sensitive design sometimes 200 lux would be adequate. It must be stressed, however, that to design for this very careful consideration of the whole visual environment is essential. By considering the impact of daylight the requirements for artificial lighting can be significantly modified and indeed there is growing evidence that people function better in an environment which maximises the use of natural lighting.

Glare

In the working or leisure environment it is essential that there is sufficient light available to carry out the tasks efficiently but glare is limited. Glare can be a problem in spaces where there is a large contrast between one vertical surface and another. A classic example is a window with a dark (say dark blue) wall covering adjacent to it. This gives contrast glare, which can be very disturbing to the occupant. To minimise glare it is essential to ensure that dark and light areas adjacent to each other are minimised and that reflections from light fittings, the sun, windows etc. are not visible in computer screens.

Noise

Noise in internal spaces comes from two main sources: external and internal. External noise sources (traffic etc.) should be considered when the building relies on natural ventilation systems, as open windows will allow this noise to enter the building.

Internal noise can be minimised by ensuring that there are plenty of soft finishes within the space and also by preventing the space looking like a long thin corridor with a hard finishes. This type of space is sometimes seen in naturally ventilated spaces with exposed concrete ceilings. Noise emitted at one end of the space is then easily reflected to other parts of the space.

Internal heat gains

Internal heat gains always add complexity to a design and steps should be taken to minimise them. Where possible areas where high gains are possible should be grouped together so that they can be dealt with by appropriate service systems.

The main gains are outlined below.

People

Each occupant of an office will produce between 100 and 600 W of heat every hour and the greater the occupant density the greater will be the load. Densities of about $8–10\,m^2$ per person are generally regarded as being satisfactory.

Equipment

Heat gains from equipment are very important in the design of the building services required to deal with them. Computers are now considered as being a major contributor to these gains and building services designers generally take the maximum number of computers in the space as the computing load. However, there is strong evidence from studies carried out at the Building Research Establishment that these loads are significantly overestimated and also no consideration is taken into account of the move away from cathode ray computer screens to flat screen LCD types which have significantly lower energy consumption. Other sources of heat are cold water, coffee, snack or drinks machines, printers and photo-booths etc., and to minimise their impact they should be positioned in the same locality.

Building design

The design of the building can play a significant role in the operational efficiency of the project and the main contributors to this are as follows.

Plan form

Plan form has a very significant role in the design for energy efficiency. Deep plan forms will result in the building requiring a larger proportion of the floor area to be artificially lit and more reliance on mechanical cooling. It is generally accepted that a space up to about 6 m deep from a window will be able to take advantage of natural lighting and natural ventilation and if natural ventilation is a prerequisite of the design than about 14 m deep is regarded as the upper limit for the floor slab.

Orientation

Building orientation can play a significant role in determining the solar gains received. A building facing east or west will be more susceptible to receiving adverse low altitude sunlight in the morning and evening, which will contribute to likely overheating of these zones within the building. Low altitude sunlight is always more difficult to deal with than the higher altitudes during the middle part of the day and therefore by minimising glazing on the east–west façades and providing solar shading of the south the potential adverse effects of solar penetration can be minimised.

Glazing ratios

Glazing ratios have an important role to play in the design of building façades. Windows let in light and solar heat and lose heat to the outside. The larger the window the more daylight and solar gain will enter and the larger the losses will be. There is an optimum design of glazing systems, which attempts to provide a balance between these energy flows. This balance is a function of the orientation, location, obstructions and user requirements. Generally, between 25% and 45% ratios are regarded as being the optimum, depending on the above factors.

Window design for solar protection
To prevent overheating windows should always be protected from direct solar gains and external shading is recommended. Internal shading only serves to redirect the gains to the space as they are already in the space, having passed through the glass.

Window design for daylight
The qualities of daylight are such that it should always receive serious consideration in any design analysis, as there is strong evidence that occupants prefer to work in a day lit environment. Daylight also offsets the need for artificial lighting.

Window design for natural ventilation requirement
Windows are the main source of natural ventilation and if this is required in the design then the choice of window can significantly affect the provision of ventilation. Windows that open in such a way as to provide draughts are to be avoided. Tilting windows generally are regarded as being the best type to use. If night cooling is required then some form of trickle ventilation is required and these can be

provided either by devices such as trickle-vents or small clearstory openings.

Thermal insulation

Building regulations require that high standards and integrity of thermal insulation are provided and it should be normal practice to carry this out. However, with the move to even tighter thermal regulation standards, designers should be actively thinking of designing buildings with thermal insulation standards in excess of the current ones as their buildings will (it is hoped) have a life span of several tens of years and over that time the likelihood of the standards being improved is very strong.

Thermal storage

Thermal storage is an important of design when the specification requires that the amount of mechanical cooling is to be minimised. Exposed thermal mass in a building is able to absorb a proportion of the heat gains produced during the working period and to remove them at night by allowing the cooler outside air to pass over the surfaces. Generally it is accepted that by exposing the thermal mass in a building, a 2–4°C drop in the inside peak internal air temperature experienced during the day can be achieved. It is important to consider other factors such as noise transmission when exposing the thermal mass.

Mechanical services design

There is evidence from post-occupancy analysis studies that often the capacity of the mechanical services systems is oversized by a factor as much as 2.5 times the requirement. There are several reasons involved in this, mostly due to safety margins and the move towards modular units with specific capacities. However, by careful consideration of the type of system to be used some of these inefficiencies can be minimised.

Plant efficiency

The efficiency of most mechanical plant is dependent of the proportion of the design load being delivered. For example, a boiler operating at say 25% of its design capacity will have an efficiency some 10–20% below its efficiency at full load. This is the main reason why modules with lower individual capacities are specified in buildings. Similarly fans have a range of efficiencies depending on the load that they are delivering. Variable speed fans should be used when the delivery of air is not constant but varies according to the demand. Electric motors and pumps operate in a similar way and again variable speed motors should be specified where possible.

Type of system

(a) *Full air conditioning*. This type of system is the most energy intensive and should be avoided if at all possible. Careful design of the fabric of the building quite often means that full air conditioning is not required. If it is required then the main issues for designers at the concept stage of the design are to ensure that the service runs are simple and adequately provided for in terms of voids, and plant rooms are provided with appropriate dimensions and are suitably located. These simple considerations can be very important in the subsequent detail design.

(b) *Partial air conditioning*. If part of the building requires air conditioning then steps should be taken to ensure that those areas are adequately isolated from the rest of the building and where possible grouped together to ensure efficiency in distribution.

(c) *Mechanical ventilation*. The transport of air through ductwork is not only space intensive but can cause noise problems in buildings. For this to be carried out as efficiently as possible, ensure that the duct runs are kept simple with bends, contractions etc. kept to a minimum. Space should be left for the ductwork and the velocity in the duct kept to about 6 m/s. Distribution within the space is also important, as draughts should be avoided. Often under-floor plenums are used to deliver air to the space through floor-mounted grilles. These floor-mounted grilles provide fresh air to the occupants' feet and if not carefully designed can cause draughts. However, they are very easy to move and this makes them attractive when office layouts are changed.

(d) *Mixed mode ventilation*. An increasingly popular system for naturally ventilated buildings. For the majority of the year the building relies on natural ventilation to provide air to the space. If necessary, this air is heated by a wet heating system. In hot weather air is extracted from the building via an extraction system, usually up the centre of the building. Outside air is drawn in through windows.

(e) *Natural ventilation.* This is the simplest system which can be incorporated in a design. These systems have been used for hundreds of years quite effectively but in the complex designs of today to produce a good naturally ventilated design may require a great deal of design consideration. The functions being carried out within buildings are often energy intensive, requiring that the heat generated must be removed to prevent overheating occurring. Care should be taken with respect to the outside air quality as it is not helpful if the building relies on polluted outside air for ventilation.

Environmental issues

Ensuring that sustainability is included in the design of a new building or refurbishment of an existing building

Often the client will be unaware of or only have a rough idea of what sustainability actually is and in such cases it will be difficult to ensure that these issues are included in the project. To help overcome these problems it will be necessary for both the architect and the client to have a clear understanding of what issues are important in the project. It will rarely be possible to include every item associated with sustainable design because of constraints such as location, funding, availability of appropriate materials etc., and therefore it will be advisable to draw up an action plan to ensure that identified and achievable sustainability is included not only in the design process but also in the implementation and operation of the building. To ensure that such issues are at least discussed the action list shown in Chart 1.1 indicates at what stages in the process sustainability issues should be addressed, along with a clear outline of what actions need to be taken as the design progresses from concept to completion. It is clear that these issues are important at all stages in the design process and it is often recognised that changes made at the early stages in the process cost very little, usually only the designer's time, whereas

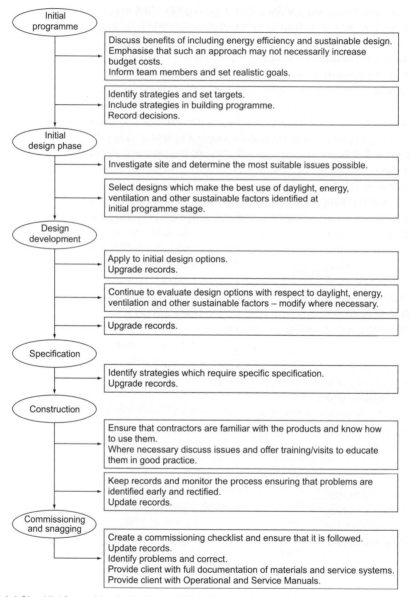

Chart 1.1 *Checklist for tracking the implementation of energy and sustainability issues in the design and operation of a building*

as the design progresses and becomes fixed any changes will inevitably cost more in both time and possible extra work.

Setting the environmental agenda

The term 'environmental sustainability' has its origins in the forestry industry where for many years it has been good practice to only use as much wood as could be grown again – in other words to live on the interest accrued from capital investments and not on the capital itself. The UN has defined sustainability as 'development which satisfies the needs of the current generation without diminishing the chances of future generations meeting their needs'. Sustainability in the built environment is often regarded as covering areas of design such as choice of materials for the construction of the building or broader issues of transport to and from the building. Somewhere in between are issues of how the occupants operate the building and what measures they take to recycle waste products. True sustainability in a building must cover other areas, which have an impact not only on the use of materials but also on the use of energy to ensure the well-being of the occupants. Therefore for a building to be regarded as sustainable or environmentally friendly the following aspects of its design must be considered:

◆ its position relative to other buildings
◆ how occupants travel to, from and within the building
◆ enhancement of the natural environment
◆ its position on a site
◆ the choice of materials and finishes
◆ the choice of building services
◆ comfort and well-being of the occupants
◆ the operation of the services systems
◆ low energy and utility costs
◆ ease of maintenance
◆ collection and recycling of wastes generated as a result of operation the building
◆ ease of reuse of the building or components at the end of their useful life
◆ social and economic impact on the community.

This list is not given in any specific order of priority and indeed there may be other local issues which have not been covered, but generally it is regarded that if the building is to be sustainable many of the above areas must be considered and acted upon. To implement all of the above is often too great a task and therefore it is necessary to establish which are really important and must be addressed and which could be ignored.

Setting the brief

It is clear that there are many aspects which could be considered at the early design stages, but in practice you are unlikely to be able to tackle all of them for a variety of reasons. It is therefore important to establish early on in the project exactly which topics are important and which are less important.

Early in the process, issues of site planning and broad concepts of building form play an important role in determining the overall efficiency of the project and early consideration can be of great benefit. Appropriate positioning of a building on a site may result in more use being made of solar energy. This can reduce the overall energy requirements of a building by a significant amount (5–10%), and at the same time give a more pleasant aspect to external spaces.

Furthermore, by considering the materials to be used, there are often benefits to be gained by recycling some of the waste products already on site (crushed concrete from old buildings used as hardcore, for example) and selecting new products with known low environmental impact.

Summary

This introductory section has indicated not only the complexity but the importance of ensuring that your designs are as environmentally sustainable as possible. The range of issues to be addressed in the early stages of the design process has been highlighted and hopefully by following these the final building will use resources efficiently and at the same time satisfy the needs of the client and occupants.

In order to ensure that such issues are taken on board by the designer it is sometimes helpful if you have an action chart to follow, and Chart 1.1 shows one way of ensuring that you are at least checking if the issues are being addressed at the most appropriate time in the project's life.

Section 2

Basic information about energy
use in buildings

Design issues for the development of an energy efficient building

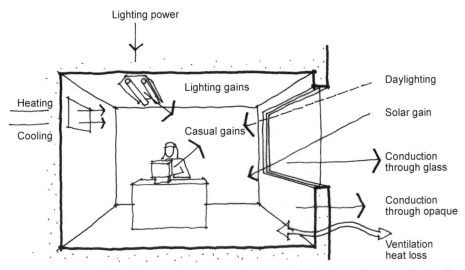

Designing for energy efficiency in an enclosure is a complex business demanding an understanding of many factors – some of which are under the control of the designer and others under the control of the occupier.

This section is aimed at setting out in broad context the main issues which face a designer when considering energy and environmental design. It is broken into three sub-sections covering the following.

(A) Comfort issues

Thermal comfort
Visual comfort

Acoustic comfort
Air quality

(B) Fabric issues

Building shape/orientation
Window design for daylight and thermal issues
Heat losses
Internal heat gains
Structural thermal mass
Overheating

(C) Services issues

Natural ventilation
Mixed mode ventilation
Mechanical ventilation including heart recovery
Air conditioning systems
Artificial lighting

Introduction

Designing a building to be energy efficient can be seen as a daunting task if we do not understand the relative importance of each factor which contributes to achieving these efficiencies. For example, there is no point in insisting on a particular lighting level in a space if we do not know what the likely effects are on either the visual environment or the performance of the occupiers of this space. Therefore before we evaluate a design it is necessary to be able to identify and understand the issues, which are of importance. Each of the following sections will try to explain each element and its role in helping to produce a building which is energy efficient. Incorporating energy and environmental issues into a design takes place over the complete design phase of the project and therefore it is important to deal with them at the right time in the process.

As mentioned in Section 1, the client may be unaware or only have a rough idea of what energy and sustainability actually is. It will be difficult to ensure that such issues are included in the project without a clear understanding on the part of both the client and the architect of

Table 2.1 General energy and environmental issues in relation to the RIBA plan of work

RIBA plan of work	Energy and environmental aspects to be considered
Stage A. Inception This is the initial part of the contract in which the ground rules are set and the actions to be taken include: • Set up client organisation • Consider requirements • Appoint design team • Prepare outline brief	Establish client priorities and build into objectives. The client often sets priorities based on previous experience or with some understanding of the issues involved, as quite often it is their first time at specifying a building. They will look to the architects to offer guidance, particularly before the other members of the design team are in place. You must therefore be able to handle the broad topics of energy efficiency, environmental performance and the impact of services on the design.
Stage B. Feasibility • Study client's requirements • Study site conditions • Prepare outline design • Prepare outline costs	Establish site microclimate and determine how it can be used to benefit the design in terms of solar access, wind and noise shelter. Determine if there is the possibility of using recycled materials which may be present on or near the site.
Stage C. Outline proposals • Develop the brief • Prepare outline design options • Prepare cost options	At this stage in the process consideration should be given to: • Internal environmental requirements, e.g. thermal comfort • Daylighting • Passive design • Orientation • Shelter • Form • Thermal mass • Space for services • Control strategies
Stage D. Scheme design This is usually the final stage in the process at which the brief can be modified. After this stage the design should be going forward to production drawings and obtaining bills of quantity. It is therefore important that the strategies for energy and environmental systems are firmly in place.	Firm up on the chosen strategies for the items set out in Stage C.

what issues are important. To ensure that such issues are at least discussed the action chart (Chart 1.1) should be followed as far as practically possible within the limits of the brief.

A good place to start this process is to consider the workings of the RIBA plan of work and how building energy and environmental issues relate to it. The general points from this are set out in Table 2.1.

It must be remembered that the earlier in the project energy and environmental issues (and indeed many other issues) are settled, the more the cost of these changes is minimised. This process is often referred to as value management and Fig. 2.1 illustrates this aspect of design quite clearly.

By following this process it will be apparent that it is advisable to have a level of understanding of many issues, to be able to select the ones which will have the greatest influence on the design and at the same time lie within boundaries of cost and client acceptability.

The following discussion on the range of topics which should be addressed is intended to give sufficient information to give a broad paintbrush assessment of their value. A more detailed investigation may be necessary as the design progresses. This detailed analysis will normally be carried out by consultants in the energy field and therefore falls outside the scope of this book.

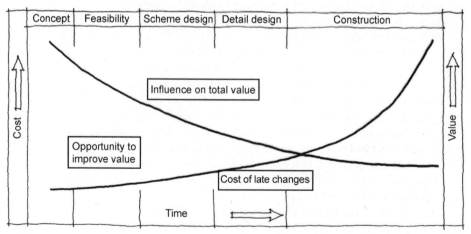

Figure 2.1 *The influence of the cost of changes to the design during the design process*

Outline of the important design issues

Occupant comfort deals not only with the thermal sensations but also encompasses other areas such as lighting, acoustics and internal heat gains. The following sections aim to give a broad understanding of these issues, which play a role in optimising the design of a building.

(A) Comfort issues

Thermal comfort

This is perhaps the most important aspect of the design, since if the occupiers are not satisfied with the comfort conditions within the building then the building will be regarded as a failure.

The human body is a complex thermodynamic machine susceptible to slight changes in the environment and through understanding the process by which we exchange heat with our surroundings we are able to evaluate and modify designs to help to maintain thermal comfort.

The human exchanges heat to and from the environment through the thermodynamic processes of conduction, convection and radiation, as illustrated in Fig. 2.2.

Figure 2.2 clearly shows that the conduction gains/losses of heat are governed by our clothing, the removal of sweat and to some extent heat by convection (air movement) and further heat gains/ losses by thermal radiation to the environment. A classic example of radiation heat transfer for humans is walking on a day when the air temperature may be in the region of 10°C but the sun is shining. The radiation gains from the sun offset the losses to the cold air and we often feel in thermal comfort. Conversely in a building with a large north-facing window, which in winter could be several degrees cooler than the other internal surfaces in the building, a person sitting near this window could feel cold even though the air temperature is adequate because of cold radiation exchange between the person and the window. Comfort levels can also be affected by air motion – in a building where the internal air temperature could be in the region of 26–27°C, a person could feel comfortable if there is sufficient air movement. It is clear that this is a complex issue and no matter what design decisions are taken there is always the likelihood of some

Figure 2.2
The thermal exchanges which take place between the body and the environment

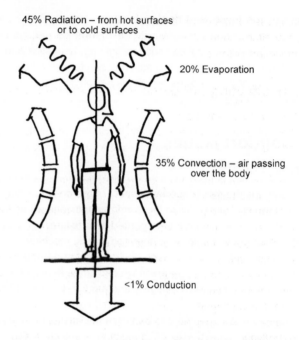

45% Radiation – from hot surfaces or to cold surfaces

20% Evaporation

35% Convection – air passing over the body

<1% Conduction

mismatch between the perception of comfort and the design intention.

Humans consider the environment comfortable if no thermal discomfort is present. The first comfort condition is thermal neutrality, which means that a person feels neither too warm nor too cold.

When the skin temperature falls below 34°C, our cold sensors begin to send impulses to the brain; and as the temperature continues to fall, the impulses increase in number. The number of impulses is also a function of how quickly the skin temperature falls – rapid temperature drops result in an increase in the number of impulses being sent.

Similarly, the heat sensor in the hypothalamus sends impulses when the temperature exceeds 37°C and, as the temperature increases, the number of impulses increases. It is believed that it is the signals from these two sensor systems that form the basis for our evaluation of the thermal environment.

The brain's interpretation of the signals is assumed to be like a tug-of-war, with the cold impulses at one end of the rope and the warm impulses at the other. If the signals on both sides are of the same magnitude, thermal neutrality exists; if not, the human either feels too warm or too cold.

Factors affecting our perception of thermal comfort

Metabolic rate estimation

In all thermal comfort studies it is recognised that the metabolic rate and clothing levels of the occupants plays a significant role in the sensation of thermal comfort.

The metabolism is the body's motor, and the amount of energy released by metabolism is dependent on the amount of muscular activity. Normally, all muscle activity is converted to heat in the body, but during very hard physical work some of the energy produced is stored in the body in the form of potential energy.

Traditionally, metabolism is measured in Met (1 Met $= 58.15$ W/m^2 of body surface). A normal adult has a surface area of 1.7 m^2, and a person in thermal comfort with an activity level of 1 Met will thus have a heat loss of approximately 100 W. The lowest metabolism occurs while we are sleeping (0.8 Met) and is at its highest during sporting activities, where 10 Met is frequently reached. A few examples of metabolic rates for different activities are shown in Fig. 2.3.

Clo value calculations

Clothing reduces the body's heat loss. Therefore, clothing is classified according to its insulation value. The unit normally used for measuring clothing's insulation is the Clo unit (1 Clo $= 0.155$ m^2 °C/W). The Clo scale is designed so that a naked person has a Clo value of 0.0 and someone wearing a typical business suit has a Clo value of 1.0. Some normal Clo values are shown in Fig. 2.4.

Air velocity

The faster air passes over the body, the more its ability to remove heat by convection is increased. If the air speed is too high then we feel a draught and if too low we feel stuffy. The general consensus is that air velocities over the body within the range 0.1 to about 1.5 m/s are regarded as being acceptable for comfort.

Figure 2.3
*Examples of Met rates
related to activity*

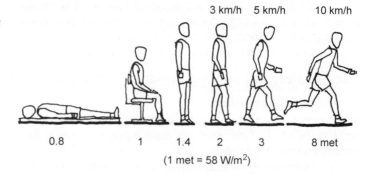

3 km/h 5 km/h 10 km/h

0.8   1   1.4   2   3   8 met

$(1 \text{ met} = 58 \text{ W/m}^2)$

Figure 2.4
Some Clo values

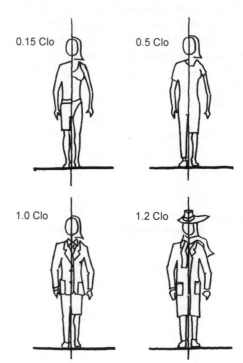

0.15 Clo   0.5 Clo

1.0 Clo   1.2 Clo

Air humidity

One of the mechanisms by which the body loses heat is evaporation
of moisture from the skin. As the humidity of the air increases, this
ability is reduced and eventually ceases when very high humidities

are reached. However, for this to happen then the humidity will need to be in the high 90% range for a significant amount of time. It is not normal to find such conditions in buildings, but at percentage humidity levels in the upper 70s to low 80s then we will experience a reduction in evaporation and we will start to sweat. One way to help the evaporation of sweat from the body in this situation is to increase the air flow rate over the body.

Air and radiant temperature

Within an environment there will usually be some difference between the air temperature and the surface temperature of the walls, ceiling, windows and floor. In spaces which are well insulated and do not have extensive glazing then the differences between the surface temperatures and air temperature will be small. However, where there is a significant difference then this difference will affect the occupants' perception of comfort. To help understand this concept the term 'mean radiant temperature' is used. Figure 2.5 illustrates how it is derived.

In Fig. 2.5 it can be seen that each surface plays an equal part in determining the average. However, if for example the person was sitting near a large window with a temperature of 10°C then the mean radiant temperature would be in the region of 17°C (Fig. 2.6).

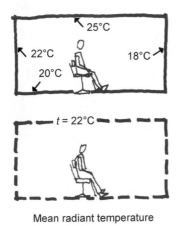

Mean radiant temperature

Figure 2.5
Mean radiant
temperature as
perceived by a person
in the middle of a space

Figure 2.6
*Mean radiant
temperature as
perceived by a person
near a large cool
window*

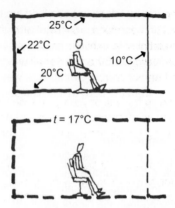

Differences between the mean radiant temperature and the air
temperature can result in a person feeling either too hot or too cool.
Research studies in the thermal comfort field have resulted in many
methods of determining whether humans will be satisfied with a

Figure 2.7
*Relationship between
some environmental
factors and thermal
comfort*

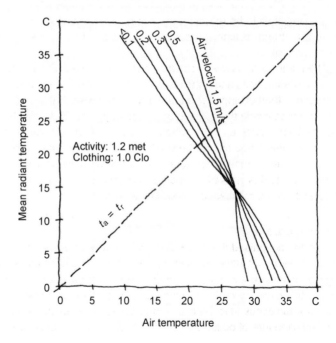

particular environment or not, but it is difficult to apply these theories at the early stages of the design process. Figure 2.7, for example, shows one such relationship between radiant temperature, air velocity and air temperature for a specific activity and clothing level. The main pointer from this graph is:

◆ If there are likely to be wall or ceiling surfaces which will be cooler (for example, poor insulation compared with other areas) then, by increasing the air temperature, comfort can be achieved.

◆ If the radiant temperature is likely to be higher than the air temperature (for example, solar gains warming internal surfaces) then thermal comfort can be achieved by decreasing the air temperature.

◆ Refinements of the two cases above can be achieved by either increasing or decreasing the air flow over the occupants.

Designing for thermal comfort and air quality

The main points to be remembered about thermal comfort are that there is a strong relationship between air temperature, humidity and air movement.

At the early stages in the design process it is impossible to give absolute assurances about the specific values of the above factors to be found in the building. For example, you may wish that the temperatures inside the building are in the range 20–25°C, but there may be issues such as large solar penetration which will affect the space at some times during the year and not at other times. It is possible to set in place simple strategies which will help to ensure that future specific design issues faced by the services engineer or occupant can be minimised. These are as follows.

Air temperature

It must be recognised that the building will have to operate for the complete year, not just in the summer or mid winter. It will experience high, medium and low outside temperatures. Thermal insulation will reduce the losses in winter and the gains in summer, so make sure that on areas exposed to these extremes care is taken in the design to limit the exposure of occupants to either high or low temperatures.

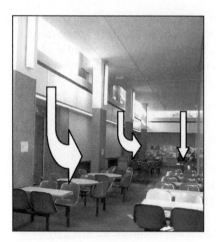

To illustrate this point, Fig. 2.8 shows a café area in the basement of a building which has two-storey glazing on all four façades. In winter the glazing will have a lower air temperature than the surrounding air (due to heat losses) which will cause the air near the surface of the glass to cool thus producing a 'cold downdraught' which will force cooler air over the seating area. Also, the cold glass will reduce the radiant temperature experienced by the users of the café thus affecting their perception of thermal comfort. The result is that there is a strong possibility that uncomfortable conditions will be evident in winter. In the summer, because of the location of the café, direct solar radiation is unlikely to penetrate to the seating but if it were positioned on the ground floor then there would be a distinct possibility that overheating would occur. Solar penetration can be a problem when occupants have to be positioned near large glazed areas, as solar radiation can increase the radiant temperature (and through absorption on surfaces increase the air temperature). Figure 2.9 illustrates this situation where an office worker is placed near large windows, resulting in an uncomfortable working environment. Internal blinds do cut out the direct solar radiation but only redirect it to other surfaces and eventually it will result in an increase in the room temperature. Although the thermal insulation standards are quite rigorous for buildings there is still the possibility that occupants can be exposed to surfaces which have different surface temperatures, and

Figure 2.9
Solar penetration can be a problem for those working near windows

when there is a large discrepancy then thermal discomfort is a possible result. Some cases, which may give rise to such conditions, are illustrated in Fig. 2.10.

Many of the studies on thermal comfort were carried out when the dress code at work was more rigorous than is perhaps the norm today. Men were usually regarded as wearing suits with ties and women similarly attired (perhaps not with ties). Today in the less formal workplace setting the dress of both sexes tends to have less thermal insulation properties and therefore both sexes tend to

Figure 2.10
(a) Large open doors allowing cold air to enter the building.
(b) High bay buildings often give cold downdraughts and if there is a large source of heat then high radiant temperatures can be found

(a)   (b)

be more susceptible to draughts and fluctuating temperatures. The seating position within a room can also affect the sensation of thermal comfort. For example, a person wearing a lightweight shirt (or blouse), lightweight trousers (or skirt) seated near an open window is more likely to complain of thermal discomfort (even if the air temperature is in the low twenties) than a person seated in the middle of the room. This spread in the range of comfort across a room has been reported many times in thermal comfort analysis studies. Increasingly designers are realising that occupants of buildings are able to tolerate a wider range in comfort conditions than those specified in the Chartered Institute of Building Services Engineers Handbook. This is a result of a better understanding of the psychology of how people react to their environment. For example, if the outside temperature is in the upper twenties on a sunny day, then occupants will tolerate temperatures in the mid twenties within their environment provided other aspects of comfort such as air movement and humidity are also considered. This type of comfort analysis is generally referred to as adaptive thermal comfort.

The British Council of Offices has adopted this approach in its specification of temperatures for office spaces. Generally in well-designed office environments internal temperatures in the region of 23–25°C are regarded as being acceptable in summer. In winter it is recommended that an internal air temperature of 18°C is aimed for, but in general practice 20–22°C is often found. The Chartered Institute of Building Services Engineers also recommend a range in temperatures to be achieved in buildings which complement the values given in the British Council of Offices publication. In buildings which are to be naturally ventilated it is often recommended that a wider range in temperatures is specified as in this case it is probable that there will be times during the year when relatively high temperatures will be found inside. In this case the temperatures and range in temperatures to be specified are given in Table 2.2. If the temperature and range given in this table are to be followed it would be advisable to ensure that an appropriate simulation exercise is carried out to determine the likely frequency of overheating occurring during the year. An overheating period is normally defined as 'a consecutive two hour period when the temperature exceeds 27°C'. It is then the decision of the

Table 2.2 *Current guidelines on setting internal air temperatures for naturally ventilated buildings*

Select design mean temperature (°C) from:

	Male	Female
Formal office	23	25.5
Informal office	25	27

Select design range in temperature from:

Design range, °C	Probable % of people in thermal discomfort at the worst time of day
2 ± 1	6
3 ± 1.5	7
4 ± 2	10
5 ± 2.5	12
6 ± 3	16
7 ± 3.5	20
8 ± 4	25

designer and client to decide on the number of overheating periods which would be acceptable.

Humidity

The humidity of the air within normal working spaces is generally not regarded as being very important. People are able to tolerate a wider range in humidity than air temperature and in the vast majority of internal spaces the humidity percentage usually ranges from about the mid 30s to the upper 60s. The vast majority of occupants are quite able to tolerate this range. However, if the humidity is in the upper sixties along with high air temperatures and no or very little air movement then the three measures combined may give rise to a larger proportion of the occupants feeling uncomfortable.

Air movement

Air movement is required to remove heat and to provide fresh air to the space. It is always a problem to design a system which will carry this out efficiently under all operating conditions. The general design specifications for air movement are that the air speed should not be above about 1.5 m/s around the body. Also design recommendations often relate to 'fresh' air quantities to be delivered to the environment. Normal design figures are in the range 6–15 litres per second.

It is difficult in the early stages of the design process to be able to quantify exactly how this ventilation will be provided but it is advisable to follow the Building Regulations with respect to the provision of openings (1/20 of floor area) as a start. Thinking about where air comes from and where it goes can often help in setting strategies to be developed later in the process.

Visual comfort

Lighting

It is essential that lighting design is considered in detail at the design stage. People are able to perform visual tasks more efficiently if they have good quality lighting, and in the working environment of today it is also essential to consider the lighting of computer screens. The normal internal environment will require lighting to at least 300 lux on the working plane, although with sensitive design sometimes 200 lux is satisfactory. It must be stressed that to design for this very careful consideration of the whole visual environment is essential. In certain conditions the required lighting level may be significantly higher than 300 lux. Lighting systems contribute to the internal loads and through careful design it should be possible to provide a lighting system with a loading of about 12 W/m^2. This figure should be aimed at. To do so, high efficiency fluorescent tubes should be used in the fittings and low wattage bulbs for background lighting. Integrating the light switching with occupancy or daylight availability will also help to control the energy used for lighting.

Glare

The sensation of glare is caused when we see areas of bright and dark patches within our field of vision. One of the most easily identified areas for glare is when using a computer. This type of glare is referred to as disability glare. In this situation it is essential that there is sufficient light falling on the screen but reflected light from other surfaces is kept to a minimum. Figures 2.11–2.13 illustrate some situations where glare could be a problem. Also glare can be a problem in spaces where there is a large contrast between the colour of one vertical surface and another, known as discomfort glare.

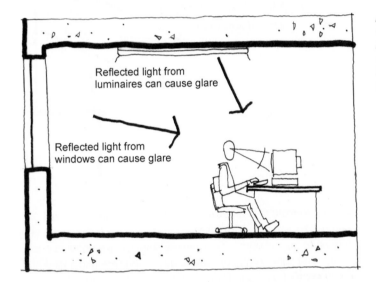

Reflected light from luminaires can cause glare

Reflected light from windows can cause glare

Figure 2.11
Operating a computer: reflected light from windows and luminaires can cause glare

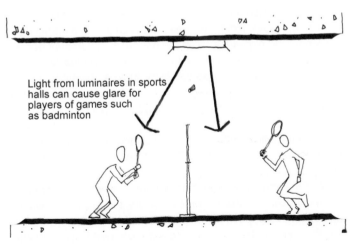

Light from luminaires in sports halls can cause glare for players of games such as badminton

Figure 2.12
Sports halls

Figure 2.13
Swimming pools

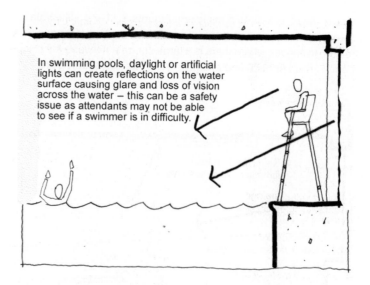

In swimming pools, daylight or artificial lights can create reflections on the water surface causing glare and loss of vision across the water – this can be a safety issue as attendants may not be able to see if a swimmer is in difficulty.

A classic example is a window with a dark (say dark blue) wall covering adjacent to it. This gives contrast glare, which can be very disturbing to the occupant. To minimise glare it is essential to ensure that dark and light areas adjacent to each other are minimised and that reflections from light fittings, the sun, windows etc. are recognised and room layouts adjusted appropriately.

A method of estimating the extent of glare in an environment, known as the Glare Index, has been developed. It is a numerical index where the higher the value the greater is the amount of glare. Typical values range from 10 to 30, where values in the range 15 to 20 are the most commonly acceptable values. At the initial stages in the design process it is not necessary to calculate the glare index but consideration should be given regarding the visual contrast which may occur.

General specification for lighting in buildings can be found in recommended design codes but Table 2.3 gives values for the more common building types.

One of the important aspects to remember when considering lighting of interiors is that in some situations there can be a wide range of contrasts within the visual field. This is particularly true in large shopping centres where there is a mixture of display lighting,

Table 2.3 General lighting and glare values for typical environments

Function	Light level in lux	Glare index
Entrances	200	19
Inquiry desks	500	19
Circulation spaces	100	22
Atria spaces	50–200	22
Atria spaces for plant growth	500–3000	–
Staff rooms	150–200	19–22
Kitchens (non-domestic)	300–500	22
Plant rooms	100–300	19–25
Car parks	50–200	–
Distribution and storage	150–500	22–25
Manufacturing processes	150–1500	16–28
Offices/shops	300–1000	16–19
Educational buildings	150–500	19
Hospitals/health centres	300–500	19
Operating theatres	10 000–50 000	–
Residential buildings/hotels	150–300	–
Sports centres	100–2000	–

Note: where the task demands visual accuracy, the higher value should be used

natural lighting and normal artificial lighting for safety. Figures 2.14 illustrate the 'confusion' in lighting in a shopping centre which can contribute to discomfort glare or in extreme circumstances disability glare.

Acoustic comfort

The human ear is able to react to frequencies from 20 to 20 000 Hz (cycles per second) but with increasing age our ability to hear the high frequencies diminishes. Measurements of sound are normally made in terms of sound pressure, which is the increase in air pressure created by the sound. Sound energy is the power per unit area and is measured in decibels. As the ear does not 'hear' sound equally across all the audible frequencies a weighting system to correspond to how we hear sound is used known as the decibel 'A' weighted scale (dBa). Figure 2.15 shows typical values of dBa for a range of noise sources. Values range from 0 (threshold of hearing) to 130 (painful sound) and a rise of 6 dBa at any point on the scale

Figure 2.14
*Illustration of visual
'confusion'*

represents a doubling of the sound pressure. As the dBa scale is not linear, it is not possible to add or subtract values from each other. In addition to defining how loud a sound is, the dBa scale can be used as an index of sound reduction potential of construction elements. Bearing in mind that it is not possible to add dBa values together to obtain an overall sound reduction you are wise to assume that the maximum reduction which can be achieved by a construction element is the value attributed to the weakest element.

One important aspect of noise control in buildings is the ability of occupants to understand speech and a rating system has been

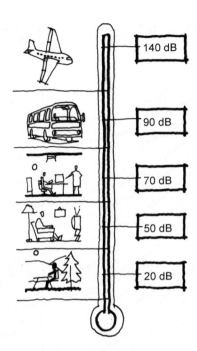

Figure 2.15
Noise ratings for typical
situations

140 dB

90 dB

70 dB

50 dB

20 dB

developed to do just that. The accepted system is the Noise Rating
(NR) system. It attempts to express equal human tolerance in each of
the frequency bands, and values are shown in Fig. 2.16.

Using the NR curves as a basis, values have been set for
maximum levels for a range of situations and an extract is shown in
Table 2.4. A general relationship between NR dBa and maximum
distance between a person speaking and a person being able to hear
the speech is given in Table 2.5.

Noise in buildings

Noise within buildings comes from two main sources (Fig. 2.17),
external and internal. External noise sources (traffic etc.) should be
considered carefully when the building relies on natural ventilation
systems, as open windows will allow this noise to enter the building.
Such noise is dealt with by providing appropriate acoustic
attenuation, i.e. solid surfaces will provide a significant degree of
absorption.

Figure 2.16
NR curves

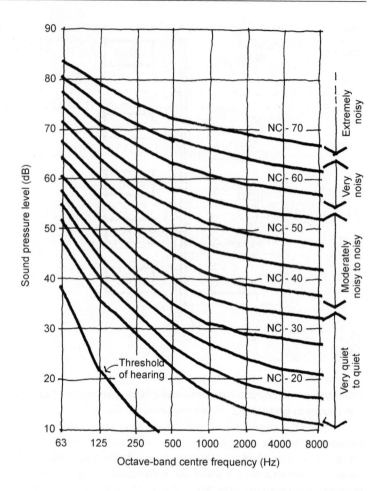

Internal noise can be minimised by ensuring that there are plenty of soft finishes within the space and also by preventing the space acting like a long thin corridor with a hard finishes which tend to reflect the noise. Long thin spaces are sometimes seen in naturally ventilated buildings with exposed concrete ceilings. Noise emitted at one end of the space is then easily reflected to other parts of the space, possibly causing a problem.

Dealing with noise at the early stages of the design process is often difficult and the calculation procedures are beyond the scope of this

Table 2.4 *An example of recommended Noise Rating for various tasks*

Situation	NR value
Concert halls, studios for sound reproduction.	20
Bedrooms in private houses, live theatres, large conference/lecture rooms.	25
Board rooms, living rooms in private houses, multi-purpose halls, libraries, cinemas.	30
Wards in hospitals, small offices, school classrooms, shops.	35
Bars, large shops, reception areas in hotels, gymnasia.	40
Computer rooms, kitchens (commercial), supermarkets, general offices.	45

Table 2.5 *Distance for speech intelligibility*

Background sound level, dBa	Background NR	Maximum distance for intelligibility in metres
48	40	7.0
53	45	4.0
58	50	2.2
63	55	1.2
68	60	0.7
73	65	0.4
77	70	0.2
Over 77	Over 70	Too noisy

book. However, by adopting the following measures noise problems can usually be minimised.

Planning considerations

Try to position the building as far away from external noise sources as possible. Care should be taken in the specification of the ground finishes – hard finishes such as paving or concrete will reflect sound whereas soft surfaces such as grass will absorb some noise.

Make sure those 'weak' areas on building façades with respect to noise, i.e. windows and doors which usually are of lighter materials than the walls, are shielded from direct noise by placing appropriate screens between them and the source. To be most effective such screens should create a significant difference in the sound path between the source and receiver as this helps to reduce the noise level. Figure 2.18 shows the effect of sound path difference on the basic sound reduction. This is not necessarily the true level of sound

Figure 2.17
Sources of noise in an enclosure

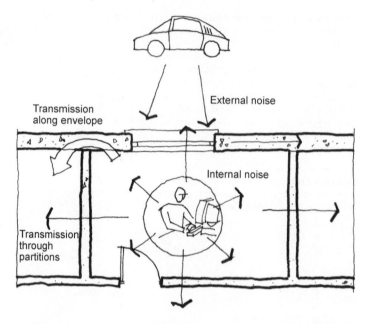

reduction as correction factors for ground absorbance, leakage round edges etc. should also be taken into account. However, it does illustrate how at the early stages in the layout of buildings on a site the likely benefits of noise barriers can be established.

Remember it is not always external noise to the site that may the most important – children's play areas can be a source of noise at particular times of the day and care should be taken in positioning sensitive areas within buildings away from such sources.

Internal planning can play a significant role in helping control noise within buildings. By looking at the room specifications it is often easy to determine those areas which will either generate noise or require quiet areas. Try to locate spaces with similar functions together and keep 'noisy' areas away from sensitive areas.

The choice of building materials will also help in reducing the transmission of noise either from the outside to internal spaces or between spaces within the buildings. Remember dense materials will absorb more noise than light materials. Table 2.6 shows for some typical building constructions the possible noise reduction potential, provided that there are no weak linkages between spaces.

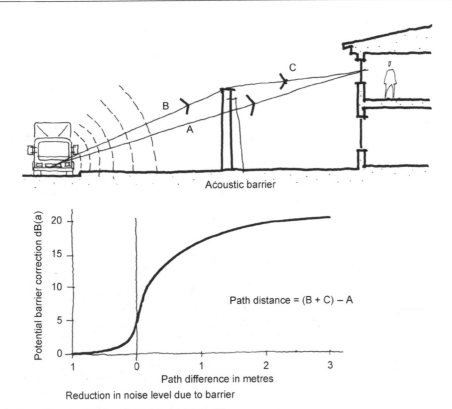

Figure 2.18 *Sound barrier illustrating the path differences*

Table 2.6 *Typical noise reductions for building elements*

Element	Typical dBa reduction
External walls	50
Open window	5–10
Sealing around window	25
Double glazed window with 200 mm air gap	43

Reverberation times

Sound emitted from a source will be reflected off the room surfaces several times (Fig. 2.19) and if the reflections continue for too long an echo will be heard. The result is that intelligibility will be impaired.

Figure 2.19
Illustration of multiple sound reflection paths in a room

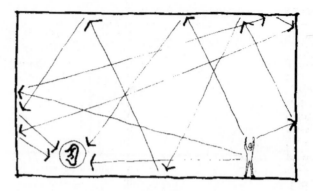

Table 2.7 *Typical reverberation times*

Use	Small room, $<750\,m^3$	Medium rooms, 750–$7500\,m^3$	Large rooms, $>7500\,m^3$
For speech	0.75	0.75–1	1
Multi-purpose spaces – schools, halls	1	1–1.25	1–1.15
For music	1.5	1.5–2	2 or more

Standards to govern this effect are based on the time taken for a sound level in a room to decrease by 60 dB. This is described as the reverberation time. Typical values for some rooms are given in Table 2.7.

To calculate the reverberation time it is necessary to know the amount of absorbing materials in the space and the simple Sabine relationship is often used.

Reverberation time (seconds) $= 0.16 \times$ volume in m^3/total absorption

Total absorption $= \sum$ absorption coefficient of materials $\times$ area

This calculation is carried out for a range of frequencies as the absorption coefficient of a material varies with frequency. Table 2.8 shows typical absorption coefficients for a range of materials.

Example of the use of the Sabine relationship
A school hall that measures $10\,m \times 20\,m \times 3.5\,m$ has a desired reverberation time of 1 s at all frequencies when 50 people are

Table 2.8 Typical absorption coefficients

Item	Unit	Coefficient at 125 Hz	Coefficient at 500 Hz	Coefficient at 2000 Hz
Air	m^3	0.0	0.0	0.007
Person	person	0.17	0.43	0.47
Padded seat	seat	0.08	0.16	0.19
Boarding on solid wall	m^2	0.3	0.1	0.1
Brickwork	m^2	0.02	0.02	0.04
Cork or rubber floor	m^2	0.02	0.05	0.1
Hard floor tiles	m^2	0.03	0.03	0.05
Plaster or concrete	m^2	0.02	0.02	0.04
Window	m^2	0.2	0.1	0.05
Curtains	m^2	0.1	0.4	0.5
Fibreboard	m^2	0.3	0.3	0.3
Suspended plasterboard ceiling	m^2	0.2	0.1	0.04
Ply panel with air gap and absorbent	m^2	0.4	0.15	0.1

present. The initial choice of materials is: walls, plaster finish; ceiling, concrete; windows, $20\,m^2$; floor, wood block.

Solution
By completing a table such as Table 2.9, the reverberation time can be rapidly estimated.

It can be seen that the room does not reach the required reverberation time at low, medium or high frequencies and therefore acoustic insulation is required.

Table 2.9

Item	Area	Low frequency		Medium frequency		High frequency	
		Coeff.	Units	Coeff.	Units	Coeff.	Units
Ceiling	200	0.02	4.0	0.02	4.0	0.04	8.0
Walls	190	0.02	3.8	0.02	3.8	0.04	7.6
Window	20	0.2	4.0	0.1	2.0	0.05	1.0
Floor	200	0.02	4.0	0.05	10	0.1	20.0
Occupants (number)	50	0.17	8.5	0.43	21.5	0.47	23.5
Air volume	700	0.0	0.0	0.0	0.0	0.007	4.9
Total			24.3		41.3		65.0
Reverberation time (s)			4.60		2.71		1.72

Table 2.10

Item	Area	Low frequency		Medium frequency		High frequency	
		Coeff.	Units	Coeff.	Units	Coeff.	Units
Ceiling	200	0.02	4.0	0.02	4.0	0.04	8.0
Walls	190	0.3	57.0	0.15	28.5	0.1	19.0
Window	20	0.2	4.0	0.1	2.0	0.05	1.0
Floor carpet	200	0.1	20.0	0.3	60.0	0.5	100.0
Floor wood blocks	200	0.02	4.0	0.05	10.0	0.1	20.0
Occupants (number)	50	0.17	8.5	0.43	21.5	0.47	23.5
Air volume	700	0.0	0.0	0.0	0.0	0.007	4.9
Total			97.5		126.0		176.4
Reverberation time (s)			1.15		0.89		0.63

Modified construction

Add carpet on top of wood blocks for the floor, change the walls to ply panel with absorbent backing.

It can now be seen (Table 2.10) that the 1 s reverberation time is met for medium and high frequencies but is very slightly over in the low frequencies. At the early stages in the design process it could be taken that this solution would be suitable subject to final confirmation as the design firms up.

Air quality

One of the issues which is of importance to building occupiers is that of the quality of the indoor air. A simple definition of indoor air quality is often taken as 'how indoor air affects the health and well-being of those exposed to it'.

This can be expanded to be a little more technical by making reference to specific attributes of the air which affect occupants. These attributes can be summarised as:

◆ thermal acceptability
◆ maintenance of normal concentrations of respiratory gases
◆ dilution and removal of contaminants and pollutants to levels below health or odour discomfort thresholds.

Much research has been and is being carried out in this field and it has been established that there may be over 900 different air contaminants

Table 2.11 Broad categories of indoor air contaminants

Combustion products
Chemicals and chemical solutions
Respirable particulates and fines
Biologics
Radionuclides
Odours resulting from any of the above

present in indoor environments. Of course not all will be present in every building but nevertheless there is scope to try to ensure that those that are present are kept to a minimum. These indoor air contaminants can be placed into broad categories as listed in Table 2.11, and have been blamed for a wide range of loosely connected symptoms often known as sick building syndrome. Sick building syndrome can be defined as a persistent set of symptoms occurring in greater than 20% of those exposed, with causes not recognisable and complaints or symptoms relieved after exiting the building. Sick building syndrome diagnosis is primarily based on the exclusion of other diseases. In contrast, there is as range of clinically recognisable building related illnesses which are a direct result of exposure to indoor contaminants and a selection of these is listed in Table 2.12.

Table 2.12 Examples of building related illness

Disease	Cause
Pontiac fever. An acute, self-limited, febrile, no pneumonic illness with an incubation period of 36 hours.	*Legionella* spp (bacteria)
Legionnaire's disease. Life-threatening bronchopneumonia with an incubation period of two to ten days.	*Legionella pneumophilla* (bacteria)
Hypersensitivity pneumonitis. Acute extrinsic allergic alveolitis.	Moulds, bacteria, organic dusts, organic chemicals, metallic fumes and dusts, animal danders, aerosolised proteins
Humidifier fever. A type of hypersensitivity pneumonia.	Fungi, bacteria, protozoa, microbial endotoxins, arthropods
Sick building syndrome.	Usually by excluding the above

Indoor air quality (IAQ) issues are important and often not taken into consideration by designers as it is often assumed that they are covered by design guidelines. However, IAQ issues are important when considering low energy design or designs which rely on natural ventilation where it is not possible to be prescriptive about exactly how much fresh air will enter the building to dilute these sources. Designers therefore need to be aware of the sources of such pollutants and be willing to take these into consideration when specifying the material finishes or other aspects of the design of indoor environments.

Carbon dioxide levels

Increasingly, carbon dioxide levels within the spaces are taking into consideration by designers. High carbon dioxide levels have been shown to be a major cause of people feeling tired or lethargic. By ensuring that the levels are kept low, the internal atmosphere is regarded as being fresh. Although under recommendations from the Health and Safety Executive maximum exposures should not exceed 5000 ppm, it is generally recommended that action be taken when exposure reaches 800–1000 ppm over an eight hour time weighted average. To keep the levels below this value adequate fresh air should be provided.

(B) Fabric issues

Building shape/orientation and other site conditions

The design of the building fabric and location or orientation on the site can play a significant role in the operational efficiency of the project. It has been suggested that the energy demand of a building can be reduced by between 10 and 20% if appropriate consideration of these issues is given at the early design stage. The main aspects to be considered are outlined below.

Plan form

Plan form has a very significant role in the design for energy efficiency. Deep plan forms will result in the building requiring a larger proportion of the floor area to be artificially lit and more reliance on

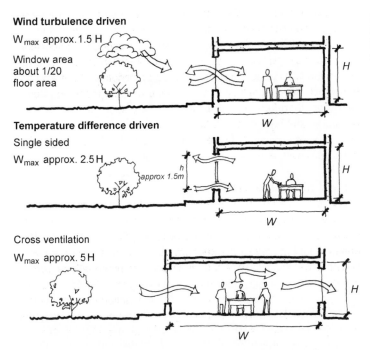

Wind turbulence driven

W_{max} approx. 1.5 H

Window area
about 1/20
floor area

Temperature difference driven

Single sided

W_{max} approx. 2.5 H

approx 1.5m

Cross ventilation

W_{max} approx. 5 H

Figure 2.20
*General guidance on
the depth of a space for
natural ventilation*

mechanical cooling. It is generally accepted that a space up to about
6 m deep from a window will be able to take advantage of natural
lighting and natural ventilation. If natural ventilation is a prerequisite of
the design then about 14 m deep is regarded as the upper limit for the
floor slab. General guidance on the depth of a space is shown in
Fig. 2.20. It is noted from this that although 14 m can be taken as the
maximum depth for natural ventilation it is possible to extend this by
having a higher ceiling. An 8 m high space could in theory be 40 m
deep.

Orientation

Building orientation can play a significant role in determining the
solar gains received, natural air flows and noise protection.
Guidance is often related to a specific site but the following may be
of some help in evaluating the potential for maximising the value of
orientation.

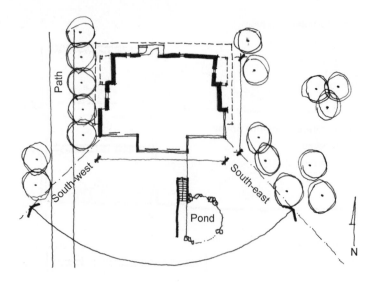

Figure 2.21
Typical design approach when considering solar access

Solar access

Figure 2.21 shows a typical solar access situation where the southeast to the southwest aspects of the building are left open to allow the sun to penetrate to the south façade of the building. The overall effect of this design approach is as follows.

◆ Leaving open the south façade allows either simpler control of solar shading or maximisation of its effect when considering passive solar heating.
◆ A building façade on the east or west will be more susceptible to receiving adverse low altitude sun in the morning and evening, which will contribute to the likely overheating of spaces behind these facades. Low altitude sun is always more difficult to deal with than the higher altitudes during the mid part of the day and therefore by minimising glazing on the east–west façades and providing solar shading of the south the potential adverse effects of solar penetration can be minimised.

Wind shelter

The prevailing winds in the UK are from the southwest and where shelter is required from these winds (either to prevent excessive heat

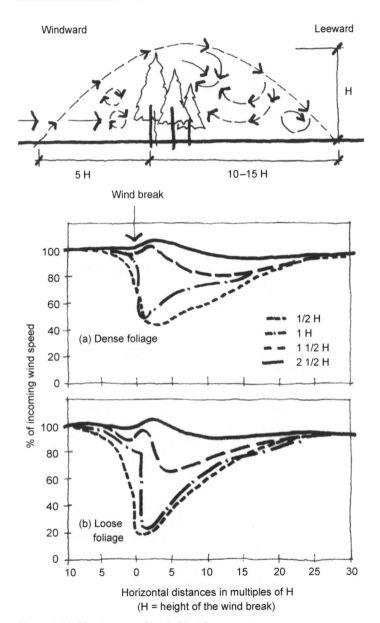

Figure 2.22 *Effectiveness of a wind break*

losses or to protect sensitive areas) then some form of shelter may be required. This can be accomplished in two ways – either by other buildings or by providing shelter belts. Figure 2.22 shows typical design values for the shelter provided by a shelter belt. From this figure it is apparent that to be most effective the shelter belt should be between three and five times its height away from the area requiring shelter.

Noise shelter

Protecting a building from noise is usually carried out by means of a noise barrier, typical noise barriers found are solid fences or walls, earth mounds and other buildings.

Barriers work by either absorbing the noise or by deflecting it, which increases the path length, and as air absorbs sound the levels received at the building are reduced – see Fig. 2.18. Sometimes trees are used as a barrier and to some extent they are effective, but noise can still pass through them. To be really effective, trees and shrubs should be used in conjunction with a more solid barrier – possibly on top of an earth mound.

Window design for daylight and thermal performance

Glazing ratios

Glazing ratios have an important role to play in the design of building façades. Windows let in light and solar heat and lose heat to the outside. The larger the window the more daylight and solar gain will enter and the larger the losses will be. There is an optimum design of glazing systems, which attempts to provide a balance between these energy flows. This balance is a function of the orientation, location, obstructions and user requirements. The larger the window the more solar energy and daylight can pass through. Daylight is helpful as it will reduce the use of artificial lighting while promoting a bright atmosphere while the solar energy can contribute to overheating. By optimising the glazing ratio for daylight and solar penetration, a compromise can be reached and it is generally accepted that the glazing ratios should be in the region of 30–50% for buildings which do not have mechanical cooling. The orientation of the glazing is another aspect which needs to be considered carefully. East- and west-facing windows are perhaps those which can cause the greatest problems as they 'see' the sun early or later in the day when the solar altitude is low. East-facing windows will let in solar radiation early in the morning contributing to warming the space – which may be beneficial. However, a west-facing window will be heating the space in the afternoon when the space will probably already be warm due to occupation and therefore this may contribute quite significantly to overheating. South-facing windows will gain most heat around midday when the sun is high in the sky, which makes solar control easier. A simple method for determining the dimension of an overhang is given in the section dealing with Window Design (see page 155).

Solar protection

To prevent overheating windows should always be protected from direct solar gains and external shading is recommended. See Fig. 2.23. Internal shading only serves to redirect the gains to the space as they are already in the space having passed through the glass.

In order to understand the relative merits of different types of solar shading devices the values for the percentage of the external solar

Figure 2.23 *An example of internal solar shading – effective at preventing direct sunlight hitting people or surfaces within the space but not as effective in reducing solar heat gains as it would be if positioned on the outside*

Table 2.13 Solar gain factors for a range of shading devices as a percentage of external solar radiation reaching the inside

Shading	Type of shade	Single glass	Double glass
None	None	76	64
	Lightly heat absorbing	51	38
	Densely heat absorbing	39	25
	Coated glass	56	25
	Heat reflecting	26	25
Internal	Dark plastic blind	62	56
	White venetian blind	46	46
	White cotton blind	41	40
	Linen blind	30	33
Mid pane	White venetian blind	–	28
External	Dark plastic blind	22	17
	Canvas roller blind	14	11
	Louvred sun breaker blades at 45°	14	11
	Dark miniature louvred blind	13	10

radiation entering the building is shown in Table 2.13. It is clear from this table that external blinds are the more effective as they prevent solar radiation entering the building in the first place.

Blocking the sun before it reaches the glazing, or any other exposed part of a building, is fundamental to preventing heat gain. A good example of preventing heat build up is the work carried out by the Urban Heat Island Group at the University of California at Berkeley, where they estimated that by painting the roofs of buildings in Los Angeles white, the air conditioning load could be reduced by about 5–8%.

While solar shading must give good protection in summer, in winter when the sun is not so strong the solar protection must be able to allow sufficient light to enter the building to ensure that adequate daylight is provided and also in some circumstances allow adequate natural ventilation.

Fixed solar shading devices are designed to protect the window from direct sun at specific times of the year, normally in the summer months, but when the sun is lower in the sky in winter they are not so

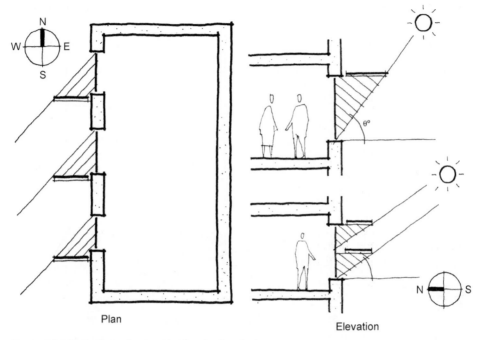

Plan

Elevation

Figure 2.24 *Illustrations of external solar shading devices*

effective. Horizontal shading devices are appropriate for shading south-facing windows but are not appropriate with east- or west-facing façades.

Figure 2.24 illustrates the type of external solar shading for both a south- and a west-facing façade. By having more than one louvre it is possible to make the length of the shade shorter. The difficulty is in dealing with the east- and west-facing façades as the projections are not above the windows but from the external walls. One way of dealing with this situation is to have a trellis work supporting plants which provides shade in the summer but will allow the sun to enter in the winter. See the case study on the Eco Centre where this type of shading was used. When determining the size of the overhang the main factor which must be taken into consideration is the time when the shade is necessary – normally this is when the sun is at its highest but it may be that the air temperature is the driving force. The sun is at its highest in the sky in June but air temperatures tend to be higher in August.

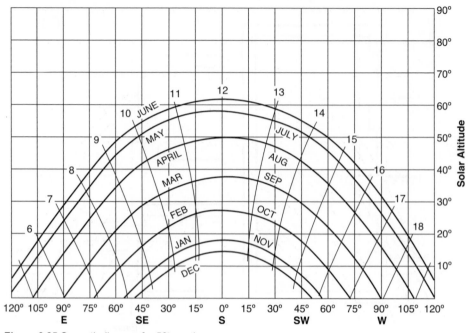

Figure 2.25 *Sunpath diagram for 52° north*

Using Figs 2.25–2.27 it is possible to arrive at a quick solution to the size of the overhang necessary to protect a window.

The procedure is:

1. Having decided the time when the solar shading is required, select the solar altitude from Fig. 2.25 or Fig. 2.26. These two figures can be taken as being representative of the UK and mainland Europe.
2. Using the altitude angle along with the height of the window, look up in Fig. 2.27 the length of the required louvre.

Daylight

The qualities of daylight are such that it should always receive serious consideration in any design analysis, as there is strong evidence that occupants prefer to work in a day lit environment. Daylight also offsets the need for artificial lighting.

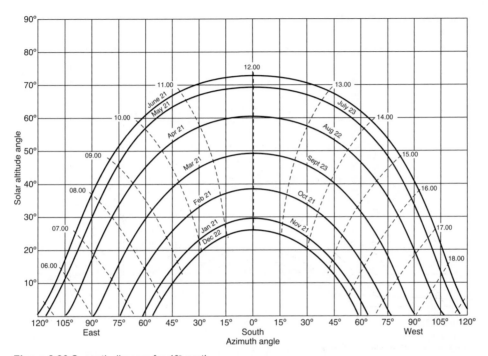

Figure 2.26 *Sunpath diagram for 40° north*

The availability of daylight is a direct function of the window size and shape and the amount of external shading present. The normal way of expressing the availability of daylight is by means of the Daylight Factor (DF). This is a simple ratio between the amount of light available outside to the amount of light falling on a particular surface. The DF is made up of three components as shown in Fig. 2.28 – direct light from the sky, reflected light from external surfaces such as other buildings and internally reflected light.

The brightness of the sky usually varies from the horizon to the zenith where it can be three times as bright as the horizon. For this reason the proportion of the sky visible from the window can play an important part in the availability of light.

$$DF = \frac{\text{amount of light falling on the surface}}{\text{amount of light available externally}} \Big/ 100$$

Figure 2.27
Length of overhang required to shade a window

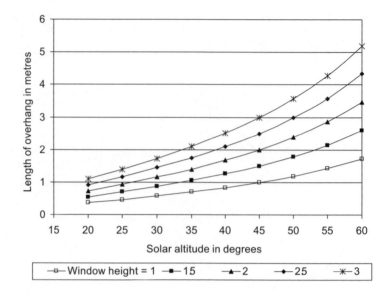

Figure 2.28
Illustration of the components making up the Daylight Factor

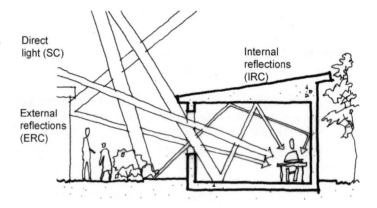

Values of the DF range from 0 to 1 but values shown in Table 2.14 indicate the general appearance of a room with particular DFs.

At the early stages in the design process it may be necessary to have an idea of what the average daylight factor for a room may be (see Fig. 2.29). This can be roughly estimated from the

Table 2.14 General recommendations for minimum daylight levels in rooms

Daylight Factor	Room appearance
Less than 2%	Room looks gloomy under daylight alone. Electric lighting is often needed during the day.
2–5%	Predominantly daylit appearance but supplementary electric lighting may be needed.
More than 5%	The room is strongly daylit. Daytime electric lighting not usually needed but with large windows there is a danger of adverse thermal conditions.
15% or more	Daylight levels to be found in atria spaces where light is necessary for plant growth.

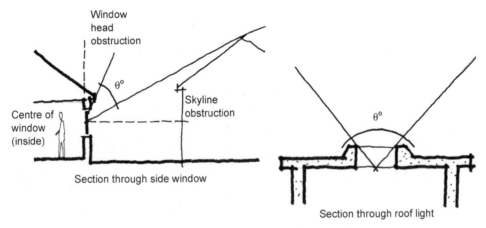

Figure 2.29 How to define an obstruction in average Daylight Factor calculation

following equation:

$$DF_{avg} = \frac{A_g \theta T}{A(1 - R^2)}$$

where DF_{avg} is the average daylight factor, A_g is the glazed area, θ is the angle of visible sky measured from the centre of the window (see Fig. 2.29 for an explanation), T is the transmittance of glazing (at design stage take 0.85 for clear glass and 0.5 for tinted glass), A is the total area of room surfaces (floor, walls, ceiling) and R is the mean reflectance of the surfaces (initially assume 0.7 for light finishes).

By transposing this equation it is possible to calculate the initial area of glazing necessary to achieve a particular daylight factor:

$$A_g = \frac{DF_{avg}A(1-R^2)}{\theta T}$$

An example of good window design is Georgian windows, which tend to be tall and thin – they allow light from near the horizon to enter the room, thus increasing the amount of light in the space. External surfaces also play a role in providing light and naturally when these are light in colour more light will be reflected from them. The same goes for the internal surfaces, and light finishes will help to 'bounce' the light around the space.

To be successfully daylit from one side the depth of a room should be limited to meet the following conditions:

$$L/w + L/h \leq 2/(1-R_b)$$

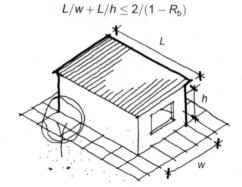

where R_b is the area weighted reflectance in the back half of the room (typically 0.5).

Daylight in an atrium space

Atria are a common type of design for large spaces and as these are predominantly top lit the Daylight Factor has to estimated in a slightly different way as shown below:

$$DF_{avg} = \frac{WT_g T_m T_f \theta}{A(1-R^2)}$$

where DF_{avg} is the average daylight factor at ground level, W is the area of the atrium roof aperture (m^2), T_g is the transmittance of the glass (0.8 for single glazing and 0.65 for double glazing), T_m is the maintenance factor for dirt (for horizontal glazing $=0.7$, for tilted glazing $=0.8$ and vertical glazing $=0.9$), T_f is a correction factor for light that is 'trapped' in the structure due to the angle of view -0.5 at the edge of the space and 0.7 in the centre, θ is the angle of visible sky, A is the total area of all atrium surfaces (m^2) and R is the average reflectance of these surfaces (usually about 0.3 or 0.4).

In many atria spaces it is not unusual to see tropical plants and these need high levels of daylight in order to stay healthy. Generally such plants will require levels of daylight in the range 750–2000 lux (see Table 2.14).

Designing for daylight — spacing of buildings

The sky component is the main contributor to the amount of light received within a space and it is therefore important to ensure that as much of the sky is visible as possible. To ensure that a space receives an adequate sky component the following general guidelines should be followed:

◆ No obstruction, measured in a vertical section perpendicular to the main face, from a point 2 m from ground level, subtends an angle of more than 25° to the horizontal.

or

◆ If the above is not satisfied, then all points on the main face on a line 2 m above ground level are within 4 m (measured sideways) of a point which has a vertical sky component of 27% or more.

Natural ventilation requirement

Windows are the main source of natural ventilation and if this is required in the design then the choice of window can significantly affect the provision of ventilation. Windows that open in such a way as to provide draughts are to be avoided. Tilting windows generally are regarded as being the best type to use. Also if night cooling is required then some form of trickle ventilation is required. This can be provided either by devices such as trickle vents or small clearstory openings.

There are five main ways in which a window can open and, depending on type, the air is distributed to the space in slightly different ways. Table 2.15 illustrates each of the window opening types and the advantages and disadvantages of each.

Table 2.15 *General characteristics of the main window opening types*

Window type	Characteristics
Vertical pivot	The ventilation capacity of this type of window is low as the opening is distributed over the whole height. For the same 22° opening as a top/bottom hung window their ventilation capacity is reduced by 40%. They can act as a wind scoop when the wind is not parallel to the façade. Driving rain can enter quite easily.
Top/bottom hung	All the ventilation is concentrated either at the top or the bottom depending on which way they are hung. Top hung windows will provide good thermal comfort in summer for the occupants but little contact with the ceiling (for night cooling). Bottom hung windows will provide good thermal contact with the ceiling but poor thermal comfort for the occupants. Top hung windows can act as scoops for warm air rising up the façade of the building. Better performance for driving rain.
Side hung	These are similar in performance to the vertical pivot windows. Can be susceptible to gusts of wind blowing them either fully open or slamming them closed. Ventilation is about the same as the vertical centre pivot windows. Where tilt and slide windows are used the tilt aspects generally do not give sufficient ventilation in summer for cooling but too much in winter.
Sliding	These windows have ventilation characteristics similar to the vertical or horizontal hung windows. Draught stripping is trickier with this type.
Tilting top vents	The opening area of this type of window is generally smaller but they provide good draught-free ventilation. They are a good choice for cross ventilation.

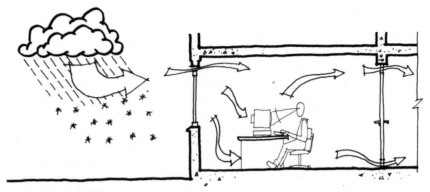

Background ventilation
In winter ventilators with an openable area of 400 mm sq. per m sq. of floor area can usually provide adequate background ventilation in multi-celled buildings. Controllable trickle ventilators can be a very effective way of doing this.

Figure 2.30 Trickle ventilation to a space

For a room to be naturally ventilated it is generally considered that a depth of about 6 m is the maximum limit but this is dependent on the overall plan form and general guidance is given in Fig. 2.20.

Trickle ventilators are designed to provide the minimum fresh air requirements to a space and they can also be used to provide a degree of night flushing of the space, i.e. promote natural cooling. They also ensure that moisture build-up is minimised. Figure 2.30 shows how a trickle ventilated space works and Fig. 2.31 shows various ventilator positions.

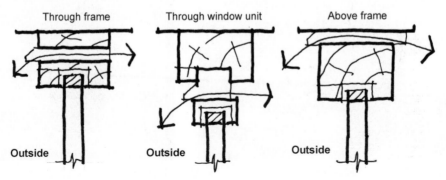

Figure 2.31 Positioning of trickle ventilators in the façade

Heat losses

Thermal insulation

Buildings lose heat in several ways and thermal insulation is one of the mechanisms which help to reduce the losses through walls, roofs, floors and windows. Figure 2.32 shows an infrared thermal image of a block of 1960s flats and illustrates very clearly how poor insulation causes large energy losses. Building regulations require that high standards and integrity of thermal insulation are provided and it should be normal practice to carry this out. However, with the move to even tighter thermal regulation standards, designers should be actively thinking of designing buildings with thermal insulation standards in excess of the current ones as their buildings will have a life span of several tens of years and over that time the likelihood of the standards being improved is very strong.

Energy moves from a hotter area to a cooler area and the rate of movement is determined by the thermal insulation properties of the materials. In buildings in winter, heat moves from the warmer inside to the cooler outside and Building Regulations are in place to set standards for the maximum rate at which this occurs. The term 'U value' is used to determine the resistance of a material or combination of materials to the flow of heat. The units of the U value are given in watts per square metre of surface per degree

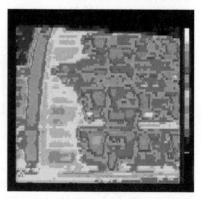

Figure 2.32 Infrared image of a 1960s development indicating high heat losses as a result of the poor thermal insulation of the fabric

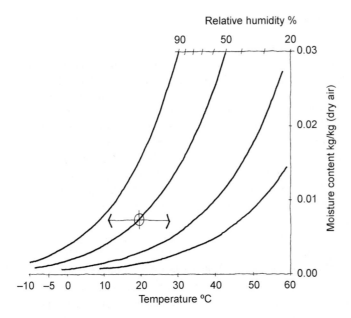

Relative humidity %

Figure 2.33
*The Psychrometric
Chart*

Celsius temperature difference across it. In practice it is relatively easy to calculate the U value provided you know certain properties of the material, but there can be some issues when moisture is present in the air. Generally the inside air will contain more moisture than the outside air and this moisture will also tend to flow from the warmer side to the cooler side. This is illustrated in the Psychrometric Chart (shown in Fig. 2.33), which is a diagram showing the relationship between temperature and moisture content of the air. It is used by building services engineers to estimate the energy loads on air conditioning equipment but it is also very helpful in understanding the relationships between temperature and moisture in air. As air at normal room temperature and humidity ($T = 20°C$, RH $= 50\%$) cools, its ability to hold moisture decreases. When it becomes saturated and comes in contact with a surface whose temperature is less than 20°C, moisture will form on the surface (condensation). The temperature at which this ocurs is known as the dew point temperature. As the air temperature increases, the ability of the air to hold moisture also increases but at a faster rate. By increasing the temperature the relative humidity decreases – meaning that this air can hold more moisture and it feels drier. Very low relative humidity can cause materials to dry out, causing cracking. This relationship between temperature and moisture is very important for several reasons:

◆ In winter when the air is 'dry – but has high relative humidity', as it is heated the relative humidity *decreases* enabling it to absorb moisture at a higher rate. The result is that any moist surface has the moisture 'sucked out'. Examples of this are our throats (we complain of dry throats in winter as the air we breathe tends to be warm but dry) and wooden products, particularly furniture, where the moisture contained in the wood can be absorbed into the air causing joints to open.
◆ In summer when the moisture levels are higher, if we cool the air slightly the relative humidity will increase, making the air 'damper', and we will have more problems removing sweat from our bodies.

Most building materials are able to absorb moisture in the form of vapour and this can pass through the surface. It is therefore very important to ensure that when designing for heat transfer that this aspect is dealt with. The mechanisms at play in heat and moisture transfer across a surface are:

◆ conduction through the solid parts of the material
◆ convection at the surfaces – both inside and outside surfaces including any cavities

Figure 2.34
The thermal mechanisms at play in heat transfer across a building element

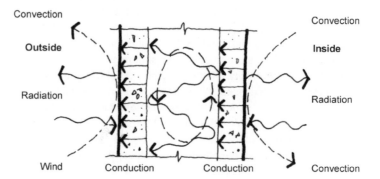

Convection

Convection

Outside

Inside

Radiation

Radiation

Wind   Conduction   Conduction   Convection

◆ radiation to or from the surfaces
◆ moisture migration through the surface.

Figure 2.34 illustrates simply how these three mechanisms act on a
wall. As heat flows across the structure, the temperature of each
surface will be dependent on the insulating capacity of the material;
but it will change and there may come a point when the temperature
of the material is below the dew point temperature. At that point
condensation will occur (Fig. 2.35). As a material takes up more
moisture the thermal conductivity is affected. Figure 2.36 shows this

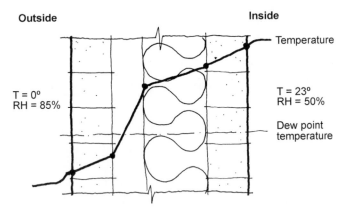

Outside

Inside

— Temperature

T = 0°
RH = 85%

T = 23°
RH = 50%

Dew point
temperature

Figure 2.35
Temperature and
moisture profiles
through a structure

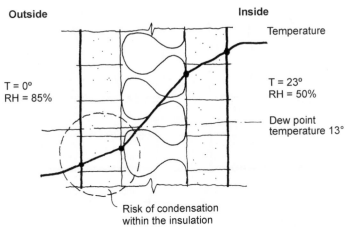

Outside

Inside

Temperature

T = 0°
RH = 85%

T = 23°
RH = 50%

Dew point
temperature 13°

Risk of condensation
within the insulation

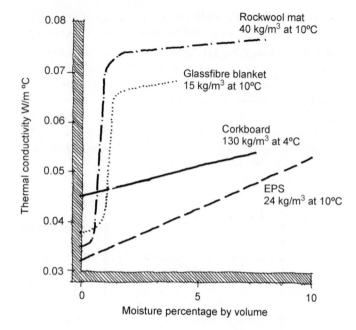

Figure 2.36
The effect of moisture on the thermal conductivity of some materials

Rockwool mat
40 kg/m³ at 10ºC

Glassfibre blanket
15 kg/m³ at 10ºC

Corkboard
130 kg/m³ at 4ºC

EPS
24 kg/m³ at 10ºC

Thermal conductivity W/m ºC

Moisture percentage by volume

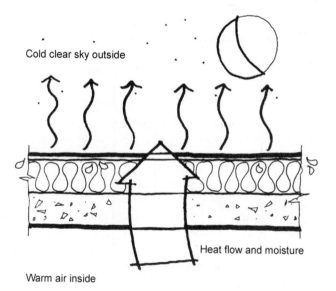

Figure 2.37
Roof structure with interstitial condensation

Cold clear sky outside

Heat flow and moisture

Warm air inside

quite clearly. The overall result is that the material becomes less efficient as an insulator and other more detrimental effects may also occur. For example, if the inner surface of the outer leaf in a cavity wall has condensation on it then there is the possibility that corrosion of the wall ties may occur or chemical actions take place in the mortar – particularly if it is lime mortar. Another case illustrated in Fig. 2.37 is in flat roofs where on cold nights thermal radiation exchanges take place between the roof surface and the clear sky, which can result in the surface of the roof cooling below the dew point temperature. Any moisture in the roof structure could condense and result in interstitial condensation.

Calculation of *U* values

General situation

It is not intended to give a complete calculation procedure to comply with any Building Regulations or Building Codes but rather to illustrate how by a quick calculation a rough estimation of the likely energy transfers across a structure can be established.

The general equation for steady-state heat transfer across a structure is:

$$U = \frac{1}{\sum \text{thermal resistances of each element in the structure } (R)}$$

The thermal resistance of a material is given by:

$$\frac{\text{thickness } (L)}{\text{thermal conductivity } (K)}$$

Heat transfer at the surfaces of the materials also takes place by convection heat transfer and therefore these resistances must also be taken into account. At both the inside (R_{si}) and outside surfaces (R_{so}) these resistances depend on the exposure of the surface and its orientation. Tables 2.16 and 2.17 show typical values of surface resistances used.

If the structure has an air cavity there will also be convection heat transfer through it and again we need to know the cavity resistance (R_c). Table 2.18 shows typical values used for a range of air cavity types and Table 2.19 shows for a range of materials typical values of thermal conductivity.

Table 2.16 Outside surface resistances

Building element	Emissivity	Surface resistance (m² K/W)		
		Sheltered	Normal	Severe
Wall	High	0.08	0.055	0.03
	Low	0.11	0.067	0.03
Roof	High	0.07	0.045	0.02
	Low	0.09	0.053	0.02

Table 2.17 Inside surface resistances

Building detail	Heat flow	Surface resistance (m² K/W)	
		High emissivity	Low emissivity
Walls	Horizontal	0.123	0.304
Ceiling, floors	Upward	0.106	0.218
Ceiling, floors	Down	0.150	0.562

Table 2.18 Cavity thermal resistances – unventilated

Thickness of air space	Surface emissivity	Thermal resistance (m² K/W)	
		Heat flow horizontal or upwards	Heat flow downwards
5 mm	High	0.11	0.11
	Low	0.18	0.18
25 mm or more	High	0.18	0.21
	Low	0.35	1.06
	High emissivity sheets	0.09	0.11
	Low emissivity sheets	0.62	1.76

So:

$$U = \frac{1}{\sum R_1 + R_2 + R_3 + \cdots + R_{si} + R_{so} + R_c}$$

$$U = \frac{1}{\sum L_1/K_1 + L_2/K_2 + L_3/K_3 + \cdots + R_{si} + R_{so} + R_c}$$

Table 2.19 Typical density, conductivity and specific heat values for a range of materials. (These values are taken from the 2002 England and Wales Building Regulations Part L and CIBSE Design Data. Where possible it is recommended that manufacturers' data are used instead of the general values in this table.)

Construction materials	Density kg/m^3	Thermal conductivity W/m^2 K	Specific heat capacity J/kg K
Walls			
Outer leaf brick	1700	0.77	800
Inner leaf brick	1700	0.56	800
Lightweight concrete block	1400	0.57	1000
Aerated concrete block	600	0.18	1200
Medium density concrete	1800	1.13	1000
High density concrete	2400	1.93	840
Reinforced concrete (1% steel)	2300	2.3	840
Reinforced concrete (2% steel)	2400	2.5	840
Mortar (protected)	1750	0.88	700
Concrete block	600	0.19	1000
Mortar (exposed)	1750	0.94	700
Gypsum plasterboard	900	0.25	800
Sandstone	2600	2.3	700
Soft limestone	1800	1.1	900
Hard limestone	2200	1.7	900
Granite	2600	2.5	900
Marble	2500	2.0	802
Slate	2180	2.0	753
Gravel	2700	0.36	840
Fibreboard	400	0.1	1400
Plasterboard gypsum	950	0.25	840
Plasterboard perlite	800	0.18	840
Ceramic tiles	1900	1.3	800
Softwood	500	0.13	2700
Hardwood	700	0.18	2300
Plywood	530	0.14	2760
Hardboard	900	0.13	2000
Chipboard	800	0.15	2090
MDF	500	0.15	2600
Wall ties (stainless steel)	7900	17.0	7500
Surface finishes			
External rendering	1300	0.57	1000
Plaster (dense)	1300	0.57	1000
Plaster (lightweight)	600	0.18	1000
Roofs			
Aerated concrete slab	500	0.16	1200
Asphalt	2100	0.7	1000

Table 2.19 Continued

Construction materials	Density kg/m³	Thermal conductivity W/m² K	Specific heat capacity J/kg K
Roofs Continued			
Felt/bitumen layers	1700	0.23	1000
Roofing felt	960	0.19	837
Screed	1200	0.41	840
Stone chippings	1800	2.0	1000
Clay tiles	2000	1.0	800
Concrete tiles	2100	1.5	850
Wood wool slab	500	0.10	1000
Floors			
Cast concrete	2000	1.35	1000
Metal tray	7800	50.0	480
Screed	1200	0.41	840
Softwood timber	500	0.13	1200
Hardwood timber	7000	0.18	1200
Soil	2050	0.52	1800
Insulation			
Expanded polystyrene board	15	0.040	1400
Mineral wool quilt	30	0.042	1400
Mineral wool batt	30	0.038	1400
Glass fibre quilt	12	0.040	800
Glass fibre slab	25	0.035	1400
Phenolic foam board	30	0.025	1400
Cork	105	0.045	1800
Woodwool	500	0.10	1000
Sheep's wool	500	0.1	1000
Thatch	270	0.09	1800
Straw	370	0.10	1000
Sawdust	145	0.08	1000
Paper	50	0.035	1300
Polyurethane board	30	0.025	1400

Figures 2.38 and 2.39 illustrate the use of these equations on simple structures.

Roof structures

When dealing with roof structures it is important to take into account the slope of the roof (Fig. 2.40) and in this situation the following equation is used for determining the heat transfer from a

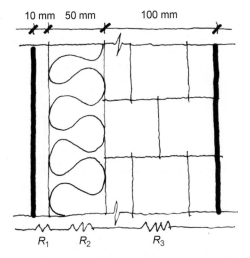

10 mm   50 mm   100 mm

R_1 R_2 R_3

Figure 2.38
Thermal resistances of a structure with no cavity

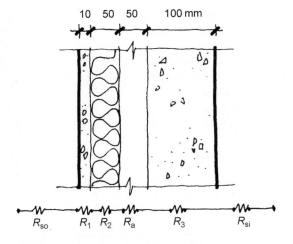

10   50   50   100 mm

R_{so} R_1 R_2 R_a R_3 R_{si}

Figure 2.39
Thermal resistances of a structure with a cavity

room through a loft and then through the roof structure:

$$U = \frac{1}{R_s \cos \alpha + R_a + R_c + R_{si}}$$

where R_s is the sum of the thermal resistances of the roof materials and the outside surface resistance R_{so}, R_a is the thermal

Figure 2.40
*Calculating heat
transfer through a loft
space*

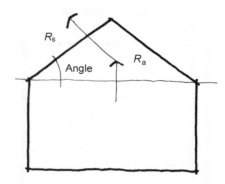

resistance of the attic air space and R_c is the thermal resistance of
the ceiling.

Ground

Heat losses to the ground can be significant and care should be taken
to ensure that both losses to the ground below the building and
through the edges are minimised. Figure 2.41 shows how heat can
flow through the ground.

When dealing with this situation it is better to use tabulated values
for thermal resistances and modify them by the percentage of the
ground covered by insulation.

The Building Regulations set out simply in tabular form what the U
value of a ground floor will be for a floor insulated or partially
insulated. For ease of use these have been reproduced in graphical
form as Figs 2.42–2.44.

Figure 2.41
*Heat flows through the
ground*

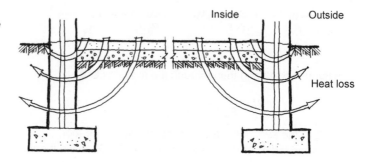

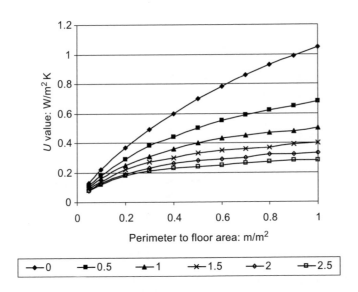

Figure 2.42
U *value of solid ground floor for a range of insulation resistances. For solid floors with edge insulation*

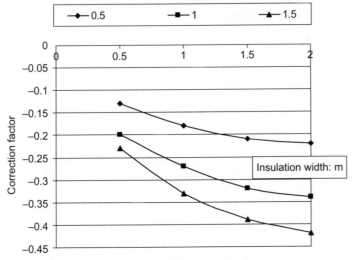

Figure 2.43
Adjustment to U *value for horizontal insulation*

Figure 2.44
*Adjustment to U value
for vertical insulation*

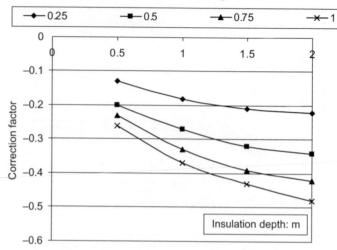

Correction factors for vertical edge insulation

Thermal resistance of insulation: m² K/W

For solid floors with all over insulation
Where the insulation is positioned either vertically or horizontally around the edge of the building an adjustment to the *U* values is made. This adjustment is found from Figs 2.43 and 2.44.

For suspended floors
As suspended floors will have under-floor ventilation which will provide a flow path for heat, thus reducing the value of any thermal insulation, the procedure to be followed takes this into consideration. In the case where the floor is uninsulated, Fig. 2.45 gives the likely *U* value of the floor.

When the floor is insulated a correction factor is necessary. This correction factor is based on the *U* value of the floor construction and set out below:

$$U_{\text{insulated floor}} = \frac{1}{(1/U_o) - 0.2 + R_f}$$

where $U_{\text{insulated floor}}$ is the *U* value of insulated suspended floor, U_o is the *U* value of floor construction and R_f is the thermal resistance of

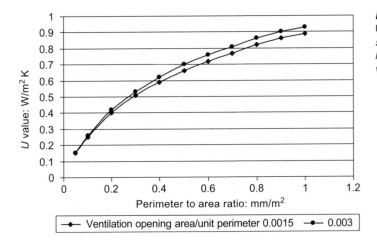

Figure 2.45
U *value of uninsulated suspended floor for two levels of under-floor ventilation*

the floor construction. $1/U_o$ are the surface resistances on the upper and underside of the floor (these normally have a value of 0.17).

Example: solid floors

A 20 m square building has a solid ground floor and it is proposed to insulate it with expanded polystyrene board 80 mm thick. The board has a thermal conductivity of 0.04 W/m² K. Estimate the likely U value of the structure. If it was decided to use horizontal edge insulation 1 m wide, what effect would it have on the likely U value?

Solution

First it is necessary to establish the thermal resistance of the insulation material. This is carried out by dividing the thickness by the conductivity:

$$R = L/k = 0.08/0.04 = 2.0 \, \text{m}^2 \, \text{K/W}$$

The perimeter-to-area ratio (P/A) is $80/400 = 0.2$.
    From Fig. 2.42 the U value is found to be 0.2 W/m² K.
    When changing to horizontal edge insulation it is necessary to modify this U value by a correction factor. From Fig. 2.43 for a width of 1 m the correction factor is -0.34. This value is multiplied by the perimeter/area ratio and the product is added to the U value for the floor with all over insulation.

$P/A = 0.2$. Correction factor $(CF) = -0.34$. U value for all over insulation $= 0.2\,W/m^2\,K$. Therefore the U value for the case where the insulation is 1 m wide is given by

$$U = U_{\text{whole floor}} + P/A \times CF$$

$$U = 0.2 + 80/400 \times -0.34$$

$$U = 0.2 - 0.016 = 0.184\,W/m^2\,K$$

From this calculation it is clear that by reducing the insulation under the floor a significant reduction in the overall U value is found.

Example: suspended floors

For the building described in the above case it is decided to use a suspended floor with a ventilation opening area of $0.003\,m^2/mm$, a thickness of 200 mm and the floor construction has a U value of 0.3.

Solution

The perimeter floor ratio was found to be 0.2 and looking in Fig. 2.45 the U value of an uninsulated floor with a ventilation opening area of $0.003\,m^2/mm$ would be $0.4\,W/m^2\,K$. This has to be modified by the procedure set out above:

$$U_{\text{insulated floor}} = \frac{1}{(1/U_o) - 0.2 + R_f}$$

$U_o = 0.3\,W/m^2\,K$. $R_f = 1/0.3 - 0.17 - 0.17 = 2.99\,m^2\,K/W$. So

$$U_{\text{insulated floor}} = \frac{1}{(1/0.3) - 0.2 + 2.99} = 0.16\,W/m^2\,K$$

Thermal bridges

Thermal bridges occur where materials of different thermal properties are put together and as a result of these properties differential heat flow rates occur. This can result in part of the structure being significantly cooler than another part. An example of a thermal bridge is the lintel over a window (Fig. 2.46) and it is possible to have condensation either on the surface or within the structure. This situation should be avoided and many Building Codes specify that thermal bridges should be taken into account when calculating the overall U value of a structure. An example of this procedure is given below.

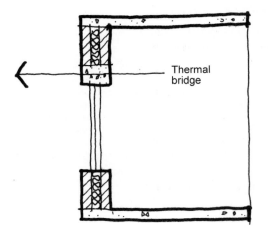

Thermal
bridge

Figure 2.46
An example of a
thermal bridge

An example of simple *U* value calculations

It is required to establish the likely *U* value of the following constructions:

An external wall

Material	Thickness
Brick	200 mm thick, density 1700 kg/m^2
Ventilated air cavity	50 mm wide
Fibreboard insulation	150 mm
Vermiculite blockwork	200 mm wide, density 350 kg/m^2
Plasterboard	12 mm wide, density 960 kg/m^2

A roof

Material	Thickness
Slates	5 mm thick, density 2500 kg/m^2
Wood wool slabs	400 mm thick, density 470 kg/m^2

Solution

It is often simpler to make up a table into which values are entered, as shown in Tables 2.20 and 2.21.

Table 2.20 Solution: external wall

Element name	Thickness t (m)	Conductivity k (W/m °C)	Resistance $R = t/k$ (m^2 °C/W)
Brick	0.2	0.84	0.238
Ventilated air cavity	0.05		0.3
Fibreboard insulation	0.15	0.05	3.0
Vermiculite blockwork	0.2	0.07	2.86
Plasterboard	0.012	0.16	0.075
			0.055
			0.123
	Total resistance		6.651
	U value (1/R)		0.15

Table 2.21 Solution: roof

Element name	Thickness t (m)	Conductivity k (W/m °C)	Resistance $R = t/k$ (m^2 °C/W)
Slates	0.005	1.8	0.0028
Wood wool slabs	0.4	0.08	5.0
			0.045
			0.106
	Total resistance		5.1538
	U value (1/R)		0.194

Internal heat gains

Internal heat gains always add complexity to a design and steps should be taken to minimise them. Where practicable, areas where high gains are possible should be grouped together so that they can be dealt with by appropriate service systems. Heat emitting equipment if grouped together can give useful heat recovery possibilities – see the case study in Section 5 on the Gasser Building in Switzerland. It is also worth remembering that it is likely that not all of the equipment will be switched on at the same time and it is worth discussing diversity factors with the client and services engineer. The Building Research Establishment

Table 2.22 Equipment ratings

Equipment	Rating (watts/hr)
Computer	50–100
Laser printer	90–120
Dot matrix printer	40–60
Medium photocopier	200–300
Large photocopier	300–600
Fax machine	40
Refrigerator	50
Kettle	10–100
Vending machine	200–750
Television	50–100

estimated that it is likely that up to one third of equipment will be switched off at any one time. Ensuring that all equipment specified uses the least possible amount of energy will not only save energy but in all probability it will run more efficiently. Table 2.22 shows typical values of energy ratings for a range of equipment found in buildings. Other sources of heat are cold water, coffee or snack machines and to minimise their impact they should be positioned in the same locality.

People

Each occupant of a room will produce between 300 and 900 W of heat every hour and the greater the occupant density and/or the activity the greater will be the load. Table 2.23 shows typical values used in design. Densities of about 8–10 m^2 per person are generally regarded as being satisfactory.

Table 2.23 Heat loads generated by people for a range of activities

Activity	Heat generated (watts)
Seated at rest	100–115
Light work	240
Walking slowly	160
Medium work/light gym work	235–265
Hard work/strenuous gym work	440–500

Structural thermal mass

Thermal storage is an important aspect of design when the specification requires that the amount of mechanical cooling be minimised. Exposed thermal mass in a building is able to absorb a proportion of the heat gains produced during the working period and to remove them at night by allowing the cooler outside air to pass over the surfaces. Generally it is accepted that, by exposing the thermal mass in a building, a 2–4°C drop in the inside peak internal air temperature experienced during the day can be achieved. It is important, however, to consider other factors when exposing the thermal mass, e.g., the possibility of internal noise being transmitted along the space, which can be disturbing, or in cases where the ceiling is not flat the possibility of visual discomfort caused by luminance distribution on the ceiling.

Thermal mass in buildings

The term thermal mass is used quite frequently by mechanical services engineers and architects to indicate that their designs are able to cope with fluctuations in internal air temperature which occur during the day due to solar gain, occupancy and equipment gains. Often high thermal mass buildings are regarded as buildings that have reasonably stable internal temperatures, typical examples being cathedrals or churches (Fig. 2.47). These buildings never seem hot in summer or really cold in winter and this is put down to the fact that the heavy materials used in their construction are able to absorb and store heat and release it slowly over a long period. This is a simple illustration of thermal mass but in buildings constructed today it is unlikely that we will have the luxury of using such vast quantities of stone, granite or even brick as was used in the construction of these buildings and we therefore need to be able to maximise the effects of this mass within current building constraints.

What is thermal mass?

A material which has the ability to store thermal energy (heat or cooling) is normally a material which has a high thermal mass. A material which cannot store thermal energy is referred to as a material with low thermal mass (insulation materials, for example). High thermal mass materials are dense and are heavy.

Figure 2.47
Typical high thermal mass building

Heat emitted into a space through occupancy, solar gains or equipment will raise the air temperature to a value higher than the temperature of the fabric of the building. If the fabric is dense then this energy is transferred to the material and stored in it and only released when the air temperature (or radiant temperature) is lower than the temperature of the fabric. As the quantity of mass increases, the potential to store heat is greatly increased and is usually able to cope with the heat inputs over long periods – think of a cathedral. By contrast a lightweight building can be described as a building where there is little or no thermal mass. Such buildings are typically constructed of materials with little thermal storage, examples being timber, lightweight block and thermal insulation. In this type of building the internal temperature will rise and fall in response to the energy inputs – **there is a greater risk of overheating in lightweight buildings compared with heavyweight buildings**.

A simple analogy of thermal mass can be illustrated by considering two spaces constructed of identical materials, say brick and polystyrene. The first space has the polystyrene to the inside and the second has it to the outside (Fig. 2.48). If both are heated simultaneously with the same heat input – perhaps a 60 W bulb – and the inside temperature noted over a period of time, we will see a marked difference in how each space responds to this input. This is

Figure 2.48
Effect of position of thermal mass on the inside temperature

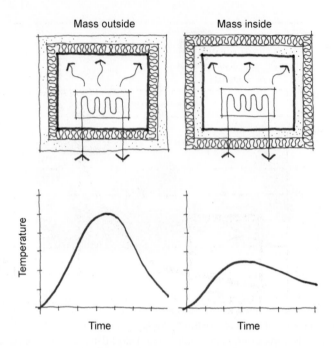

shown in Fig. 2.48, which indicates quite clearly that the temperature in the space with the thermal mass to the inside does not increase or decrease at the same rate as the space with the insulation on the inside.

This is further demonstrated in the graph (Fig. 2.49), which illustrates the relationship between the density and thermal conductivity of concrete. This relationship is general and can readily be applied to most building materials. The higher the thermal conductivity the more readily heat will be transferred to the material.

What does thermal mass do?

Thermal mass works by storing heat and releasing it several hours later. The advantages of doing this are as follows.

In winter — cool periods

◆ Heat is stored during the day and when released it can help to keep the building warm. The heat can be derived from solar energy, occupants and/or equipment gains.

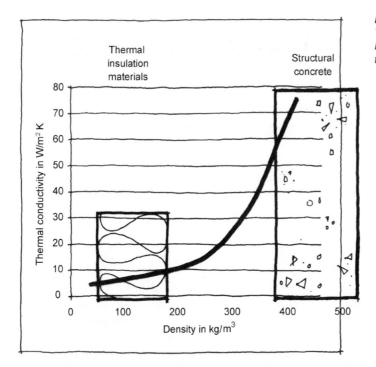

Figure 2.49
The relationship between density and thermal conductivity

◆ The inside temperature will not rise as rapidly as when there is no thermal mass. Also, the temperature will not decrease as rapidly when there is no heat input to the space – the cooling of the space will be slower.

In summer — warm periods
◆ In warm periods the internal air temperature does not rise as fast as it would if there was no thermal storage. This can help to maintain thermal comfort of the occupants for longer periods.
◆ By storing heat in the fabric the demand for cooling can either be cut out or reduced.
◆ This stored heat can be vented to the outside at night when the outside temperature is lower, thus cooling the slab and making it ready to absorb heat in the following day.

Figure 2.50
*Thermal mass in the
floor or ceiling*

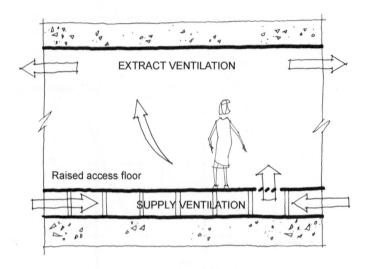

Typical positions for thermal mass are in the floor or ceiling where it is relatively easy to pass air over the surface or water through the material as shown in Fig. 2.50. In this position it is possible to supply cooled air to the floor in the evening or to pass cool outside air over the ceiling slab in the evening and night. Both methods have the effect of cooling the slab and therefore allowing it to absorb heat during the occupied period.

Thermal mass has been used for many years in passive heating of buildings and a popular example is the Trombe wall, where solar energy is stored in a high mass wall and used either to heat or ventilate a space. This system is usually used in warm climates of southern Europe or warm dry states in the USA. Figure 2.51 illustrates how solar energy is converted into heating or to provide the driving force for promoting natural ventilation.

How much should be used?
To answer this question it is first necessary to have an idea of what the energy loads are likely to be and the period over which you wish to store energy. For example, a building with low occupancy and little internal gain will require less mass than a building with large gains. Also if you are concerned about the build-up of heat

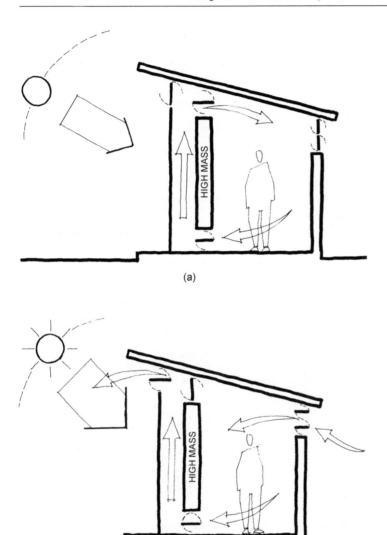

(a)

(b)

Figure 2.51 Trombe wall configurations for winter and summer.
(a) The energy from the sun warms the high mass wall, which in turn,
due to convection, draws cooler air from the space and warms it.
(b) Due to convection, the heat stored in the wall is removed by cooler
air passing over it. This cooler air from the outside helps to ventilate the
space

during the week then it may be prudent to consider storing energy over a longer period to help in this situation.

A rough calculation of the heating time of a construction is:

$$T = \frac{\frac{1}{2}(m \times c \times r_c)}{3600}$$

$$r_c = d/\lambda$$

where T is the heating time of the construction in hours, m is the mass per sq. metre of material (kg/m^2), c is the specific heat of the material (J/kg K), r_c is the thermal resistance of the material (m^2 K/W), d is the thickness in metres and λ is the thermal conductivity (W/m K).

Taking an example of the use of these equations, let us assume that we would like to establish the time taken to heat a concrete structure 100 mm thick with a mass of 700 kg/m^2.

We can assume that the specific heat of the concrete is 850 J/kg K and the thermal conductivity is 2 W/m K.

First we estimate the thermal resistance of the structure:

$$\text{the thickness is } 100\,\text{mm} = 0.1\,\text{m}$$

$$\text{the thermal conductivity } (\lambda) = 2\,\text{W/m K}$$

We calculate the thermal resistance from:

$$r_c = d/\lambda$$

$$r_c = 0.1/2 = 0.05\,\text{m}^2\text{K/W}$$

Now the time to heat the structure is given by:

$$T = \frac{\frac{1}{2}(m \times c \times r_c)}{3600}$$

the mass is 700 kg/m^2
the specific heat is 850 J/kg K, so

$$T = \frac{\frac{1}{2}(700 \times 850 \times 0.05)}{3600}$$

$$= 8.26\,\text{hours}$$

Therefore it would take just over $8\frac{1}{4}$ hours to heat this mass of concrete. In this calculation it has been assumed that the temperature rise was 1 K.

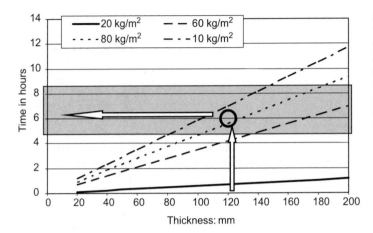

Figure 2.52
The effect of thickness and density on the heating times of a concrete structure. Note: the grey band is the normal time period used in buildings to absorb heat gains

A table of specific heats and conductivity values is given in Table 2.19 for common building materials.

From this calculation it is also possible to establish how much energy is stored in this material. We know that the specific heat capacity is 850 J/kg K, so for every kilogram of material we can store 850 Joules of energy (for a 1° rise in temperature). As the mass is given per square metre of material the actual mass is the thickness multiplied by the given mass, so actual mass is $700 \times 0.1 = 70$ kg. Therefore the energy stored is $70 \times 850 = 59\,500$ joules per square metre of surface.

You do not always want to have to calculate how much mass is necessary to use in a building and the graph shown in Fig. 2.52 (which has been developed from the above equations) indicates the rough heating times of different thicknesses and densities of a concrete structure. The normal storage times, which tend to be used in buildings, are heating times in the region of 8–12 hours. This coincides with the normal working day and means that by the end of the day the structure has absorbed all of the heat that it can and is ready to dissipate it to the cooling medium ready for the next day.

What storage capacity is necessary?

This is perhaps the most important aspect of thermal mass as heavy materials carry a cost penalty both in terms of the material itself and

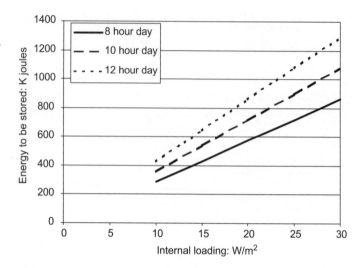

Figure 2.53
Possible amount of energy to be stored per day

also on the structural costs. The greater the amount of mass in the building the more stable it will become, but what is the optimum?

From a simple estimation of the likely internal loads it is possible to estimate the maximum amount of energy to be stored in the fabric. Based on a range of internal loads, Fig. 2.53 indicates the likely range in daily energy loads to be imposed on the space. Following on from the likely amount of energy to be stored in the

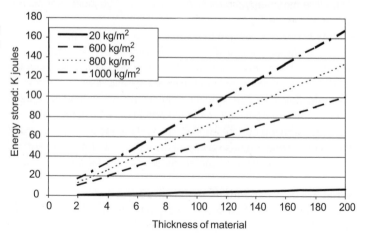

Figure 2.54
Potential energy stored in the mass element as a function of thickness and density for a 1°C rise in temperature

fabric, Figs 2.54–2.56 illustrate the amount of storage capacity in materials of different density for both thickness and the temperature rise of the material. Research and measurements carried out in many buildings indicate that the temperature of the storage elements will increase by about 2–5°C over the day. Obviously the higher the temperature of the surface the more influence it will have on the radiant temperature experienced by the occupants.

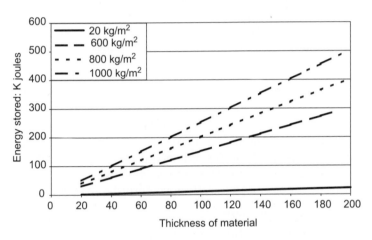

Figure 2.55
Potential energy stored in the mass element as a function of thickness and density for a 3°C rise in temperature

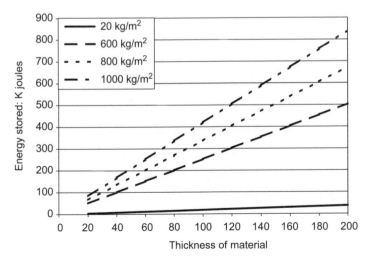

Figure 2.56
Potential energy stored in the mass element as a function of thickness and density for a 5°C rise in temperature

Establishing the exact amount of storage to design for is perhaps a little beyond the scope of this text but a rough approximation can be established if you have an idea of the amount of heat which could be removed by ventilation. This is always the most difficult aspect to determine as ventilation is so dependent on other issues, such as leakage of the fabric, wind direction/speed and whether you are using natural or mechanical ventilation. Additionally, the effectiveness of the ventilation system can play a role in determining the amount of heat which can be removed. However, bearing this in mind, a calculation procedure which will give us a rough guide to whether or not we have allowed sufficient thermal mass in our design is outlined below.

Example

Let us look at a simple example of how to roughly estimate the amount of thermal mass necessary for an office environment.

A 60 m^2 office with a height of 3 m is designed to have internal loads of 15 W/m^2. The intention is to ventilate the space at the rate of two air changes per hour. The office is occupied for 8 hours per day and it is assumed that the mean external air temperature is 16°C.

First we can estimate the total heat input over the working day from:

$$\text{Area of space} = 60\,m^2$$

$$\text{Internal load} = 15\,W/m^2$$

$$\text{Working day} = 8 \text{ hours which is equivalent to } 8 \times 3600$$

$$= 28\,800 \text{ seconds}$$

$$\text{Total heat input} = \text{load} \times \text{time load is imposed (in seconds)}$$

$$= 15 \times 60 \times 28\,800$$

$$= 25\,920\,000\,J$$

$$= 25\,920\,kJ \text{ or } 432\,kJ/m^2$$

Next we can estimate how much heat the ventilating air could remove:

$$\text{Volume of space} = 60\,m^2 \times \text{height of office (3 m)} = 180\,m^3$$

$$\text{Air change rate} = 2 \text{ changes per hour}$$

$$\text{Volume of air moved} = \text{air changes per hour} \times \text{volume of space}$$

$$= 2 \times 180$$

$$= 360\,m^3/hr$$

Over the 8 hour period the volume of air moved $= 360 \times 8 = 2880 \, \text{m}^3$

As the air passes through the space it will pick up some of the heat being generated – so initially let us assume that it rises in temperature by 1°C. The amount of heat that the air will remove per day will therefore be established from:

Heat removed $=$ volume of air $\times$ density of air $\times$ specific heat of air

$\times$ temperature increase in the air

or

$$Q = m \times C_p \times \Delta T$$

So density of air can be taken as $1.2 \, \text{kg/m}^3$; specific heat of air taken as 1006 J/kg K.

Therefore for a 1°C rise ($\Delta T = 1$), the potential amount of heat which can be removed is

$$Q = 2880 \times 1.2 \times 1006 \times 1$$

$$= 3\,476\,736 \, \text{J or } 3477 \, \text{kJ}$$

This is equivalent to $58 \, \text{kJ/m}^2$.

It is unlikely that the temperature of the air leaving the space would only be 1°C higher than when it comes in, as it will be present in the space for about 30 min (two air changes per hour). If we assume that the internal air temperature is likely to be in the region of 20°C, then we could assume that the incoming air will pick up about 4–5°C.

Let us assume a 5°C rise. This means that the potential heat removed from the space is in the region of $290 \, \text{kJ/m}^2$.

Returning to the heat generated we find that this is $432 \, \text{kJ/m}^2$, therefore the difference between these two values is the potential energy to be stored in the thermal mass:

heat generated $=$ heat transferred to air $+$ heat to storage

This means in this situation approximately $142 \, \text{kJ/m}^2$ of heat is available for storage. Figure 2.56 shows that to store this amount of heat over an 8-hour period, with a 5°C rise would need a structure with a mass of $800 \, \text{kg/m}^2$ and depth of 50 mm.

If the temperature rise was smaller – say 3°C – then the structure would need to have a mass of $800 \, \text{kg/m}^2$ and a depth of 80 mm. You can also see from the graphs that other combinations of the structure can be used.

In Section 3 a work-sheet for determining the amount of thermal mass is presented.

Over the past few years there has been growing interest in the use of thermal mass to reduce peak indoor air temperatures and many examples are available in the literature. However, you should remember that thermal mass can be used almost anywhere and even in existing buildings it is possible through simple control mechanisms to maximise its use.

Some examples of thermal mass in use

A 1930s mechanical workshop

This workshop, constructed of concrete and brick with large south-west facing windows (Fig. 2.57), suffered from overheating in summer and by simply arranging for cross ventilation overnight the peak internal air temperatures were reduced by, on average, 3°C.

Hockerton housing development

A more advanced use of thermal mass can be found in the Hockerton housing development (Fig. 2.58), where the concrete floor slab and the high density block work coupled with earth storage helps to provide a very stable internal environment.

Figure 2.57
A 1930s machine shop in Sheffield which made use of night ventilation to cool the concrete and brick structure and thus reduce the frequency of overheating

Figure 2.58 The Hockerton development near Newark, Nottinghamshire, makes use of thermal mass and earth banking to provide a stable internal environment

Very low energy office building

The head office of the building merchants Gasser in Chur, Switzerland, uses thermal mass to control the indoor temperatures. The building (Fig. 2.59) does not have a heating system and relies on simple heat recovery extract ventilation coupled with advanced glazing systems to maintain a comfortable indoor environment. More information on the design of this building is contained in a case study in Section 5.

Overheating

This aspect of design is perhaps one of the most difficult to establish at the early stages in the design process. A space will overheat when the heat gains cannot be removed by natural means.

Figure 2.59
*The south elevation of
the Gasser office
building*

Factors affecting the incidence of overheating are:

◆ glazing ratio and window orientation
◆ solar control devices
◆ internal heat gains
◆ thermal mass
◆ ventilation rate.

In order to estimate the likelihood of the space overheating, consideration should be given to all of the above factors and at the early stages in the design process none of the above will be fixed, which makes it more difficult to determine the possibility of overheating occurring. Much of the published work on overheating refers to office environments which, although important spaces, does not help when considering other types of buildings. At the early stages in the design process it is probably better to consider the effects of each of the factors contributing to overheating rather than trying to give a numerical value in terms of the number of hours in the year when the space is likely to overheat.

A rough approximation of the likelihood of a space overheating is given in the current England and Wales Building Regulations, Part L2. This procedure is intended to limit the amount of solar energy reaching the interior space and takes no account of internal heat gains from other sources, ventilation cooling or thermal mass. However, it is this method which will help to prevent the worst cases of solar overheating.

The basis of the calculation is that the space is divided into passive and non-passive zones. The passive zones are considered as those spaces which are no more that 6 m deep and the non-passive zones any spaces which are at least 6 m from an outside wall.

For both passive and non-passive zones the area of glazing (vertical and horizontal) is estimated and then, using the following tables and equations, the likelihood of overheating is estimated. To meet the requirements of these regulations the maximum permitted solar load is 25 W/m^2.

For vertical glazing

$$Q_{slw} = \frac{1}{A_p \sum A_g q_s f_c (1 - f_{rw})}$$

where Q_{slw} is the solar load per unit floor area (W/m^2), A_p is the floor area of perimeter zone (m^2), A_g is the area of glazed opening (m^2), q_s is the solar load for each orientation of opening (W/m^2), f_c is the correction factor for glazing blind configuration and f_{rw} is the framing ratio for the window (for typical windows the value is taken as 0.1).

For horizontal glazing

$$Q_{sir} = q_{sr} g_{rr} f_c (1 - f_{rr})$$

where Q_{sir} is the solar load per unit floor area (W/m^2), q_{sr} is the solar load for horizontal openings (W/m^2), g_{rr} is the ratio of total area of rooflight to floor area, f_c is the correction factor for glazing blind configuration and f_{rr} is the framing ratio for the window (for typical windows the value is taken as 0.3).

In order to evaluate these equations, reference should be made to Tables 2.24 and 2.25, which set out the numerical values for the solar radiation and correction factors for the type of glazing/blind configuration.

Table 2.24 Average solar load between 07:30 and 17:30

Orientation	Average solar load
N	125
NE/NW	160
E/W	205
SE/SW	198
S	156
Horizontal	327

Table 2.25 *Correction factors for intermittent shading*
(low e = a glass with a coating on one surface which reduces the radiation loss from the inside of a building to the outside)

Glazing/blind configuration – from inside to outside	Correction factor f_c
Blind – clear – clear	0.95
Blind – clear – reflecting	0.62
Blind – clear – absorbing	0.66
Blind – low e – clear	0.92
Blind – low e – reflecting	0.6
Blind – low e – absorbing	0.62
Clear – blind – clear	0.69
Clear – blind – reflecting	0.47
Clear – blind – absorbing	0.5
Clear – clear – blind – clear	0.56
Clear – clear – blind – reflecting	0.37
Clear – clear – blind – absorbing	0.39
Clear – clear – blind	0.57
Clear – clear – clear – blind	0.47

Example of the use of this procedure

A proposed single storey school with an east–west orientation, 50 m long, 12 m deep, with a storey height of 3 m, has the following glazing systems:

45% standard double glazing on the south façade with internal blinds
0% glazing on the east and west façades
20% standard double glazing on the north façade with internal blinds

Solution

South façade

$$A_p \text{ (floor area zone)} = 300 \, (\text{m}^2)$$
$$A_g \text{ (area of glazed opening)} = 67.5 \, (\text{m}^2)$$
$$q_s \text{ (from Table 2.24)} = 156 \, (\text{W/m}^2)$$
$$f_c \text{ (from Table 2.25)} = 0.95$$
$$f_{rw} = 0.1$$
$$Q_{slw} = 1/300 \times [67.5 \times 156 \times 0.95 \times (1 - 0.1)]$$
$$= 30 \, \text{W/m}^2$$

This value does not meet the requirements of the Regulations, so let's move the blind from the inside to the outside. In this case the value of f_c changes to 0.57, which, when the calculation is carried out again, gives a solar load of 18 W/m², which *does* meet the requirements.

North façade

$$A_p \text{ (floor area zone)} = 300 \, (\text{m}^2)$$

$$A_g \text{ (area of glazed opening)} = 30 \, (\text{m}^2)$$

$$q_s \text{ (from Table 2.24)} = 125 \, (\text{W/m}^2)$$

$$f_c \text{ (from Table 2.25)} = 0.95$$

$$f_{rw} = 0.1$$

$$Q_{slw} = 1/300 \times [30 \times 125 \times 0.95 \times (1 - 0.1)]$$

$$= 10.68 \, \text{W/m}^2$$

This meets the requirement without any alteration.

This calculation procedure is easy to carry out and gives a quick but rough estimate of the potential for overheating of a space. It is particularly useful when debating either the type of glass or glass blind configuration to be used in a particular design.

(C) Services issues

The services issues to be covered in this section will deal with the supply of warm/cool air and artificial lighting to a building. These outlines will deal in general principles only, as at the early stages in the design process the detail workings of the systems are not required; rather, a general feeling as to how, where and what space should be left are the main requirements of the designer. The systems to be covered include:

◆ natural ventilation
◆ mixed mode ventilation
◆ mechanical ventilation including heart recovery
◆ air conditioning systems
◆ artificial lighting.

General background

There is evidence from post-occupancy analysis studies that mechanical services systems are often oversized by a factor as much as 2.5 times their requirement. Several factors are involved in this oversizing, mostly the result of safety measures to meet a defined performance specification and/or the use of modular systems which come in specific sizes. However, by careful consideration at the early design stage of the type of system to be used some of these inefficiencies can be minimised.

The efficiency of most mechanical plant is dependent of the proportion of the design load being delivered. For example, a boiler operating at say 25% of its design capacity will have an efficiency some 10–20% below its efficiency at full load. This is perhaps the main reason why modular systems are specified in buildings. Similarly fans have a range of efficiencies depending on the load they are delivering. There is a wide range of options open to the services designer when choosing equipment to run efficiently, perhaps the most common being variable speed motors. Such devices operate at high efficiencies over a wide range of delivery flows whether delivering air or liquids. There are over 25 different mechanical services systems which can be installed in a building and indeed there is no one correct way to service a building. Most buildings can be adequately supplied with heat/cooling by a range of systems. The main issue is therefore selecting the system which satisfies the architectural design, operation of the building and cost restraints in the most efficient way. The main types of service systems to be found in buildings will be broadly outlined in the following sections. Sometimes there is confusion in the terminology used in mechanical services design. Air conditioning is normally understood to mean the control of

- air temperature (heating and cooling)
- air humidity
- filtration
- delivery of air to the space.

But sometimes the term air conditioning is used in any situation where air is being supplied to the building without regard to the processes through which it as passed.

Natural ventilation

As the name suggests, this is a natural system and air is supplied and extracted by wind and buoyancy forces. The larger the windows the more effective the ventilation will be. However, to make natural ventilation work effectively it will also be necessary to have openings at both low and high levels within the building – this is to promote the buoyancy or stack effect (Fig. 2.60).

In order to promote natural ventilation the internal plan form of the building should be kept as simple as possible – open plan spaces are the best as they offer little resistance to air flows, whereas highly partitioned spaces reduce the ability of the air to flow across or up the building.

One of the main issues in natural ventilation of buildings is to ensure that the air being supplied to the building is 'clean' and in built up areas this can be a problem.

The issues which affect the viability of a natural ventilation system are set out below:

◆ where the air comes from – polluted or fresh
◆ the window design – efficient distribution of air or not
◆ flow path through the building – partitioned spaces offer higher resistance
◆ exhaust paths – could be a stack or windows – if a stack remember that it could be physically large (see the ECO Centre case study in Section 5)
◆ other outlets – will the extracted air cause problems to others?
◆ the system should be able to satisfy the needs of people not located near a window
◆ the furniture layout should permit easy access to the windows
◆ the open windows must not interfere with the operation of blinds
◆ fire compartmentation or smoke control must be respected
◆ avoid noise from traffic or fumes
◆ try to draw air from shaded sides of the building.

For many of the above design issues there is no one answer as they are building specific but the ones which are adjustable at the early design stages are:

◆ the shape orientation and depth of the building
◆ the internal layout

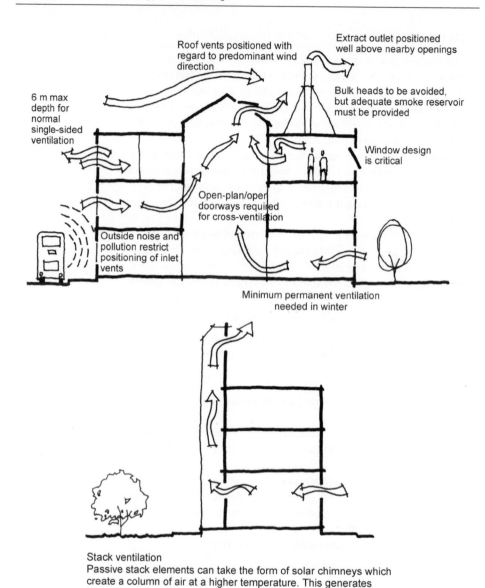

Roof vents positioned with regard to predominant wind direction

Extract outlet positioned well above nearby openings

6 m max depth for normal single-sided ventilation

Bulk heads to be avoided, but adequate smoke reservoir must be provided

Window design is critical

Open-plan/open doorways required for cross-ventilation

Outside noise and pollution restrict positioning of inlet vents

Minimum permanent ventilation needed in winter

Stack ventilation
Passive stack elements can take the form of solar chimneys which create a column of air at a higher temperature. This generates higher pressure differences and so further enhances the stack effect. A passive stack can also be generated through an atrium, which will additionally act as a buffer to reduce fabric heat loss.

Figure 2.60 *The general issues in providing natural ventilation to a building*

◆ the provision of flow paths for the air – either atrium spaces, stacks or windows.

Perhaps the main question to be asked about natural ventilation design is – *how large should the openings be*? To answer this properly would need an understanding of the micro-climate of the site. By adopting the procedure set out in the 'The Chartered Institute of Building Service Engineers Applications Manual AM10', a simplified calculation for estimating the size of windows for a naturally ventilated building can be carried out. The relationship is:

$$Q/A = C_d[2 \times g(h_{npl} - h)[(T_{ins} - T_{out})/T_{ins}]]^{1/2}$$

where Q/A is the volume flow rate to area of opening ($m^3\,s^{-1}/m^2$), C_d is the discharge coefficient (usually taken as 0.61), g is the acceleration due to gravity (9.81 m/s^2), h is the height of opening (m), h_{npl} is the height of neutral pressure (m), T_{ins} is the inside temperature (K) and T_{out} is the outside temperature (K).

The neutral pressure line is not exactly defined for every building but for natural ventilation to occur it must be above the ceiling height of the highest floor. A reasonable assumption is that this neutral pressure line is about 0.25 m above the highest ceiling.

Using this relationship, Figs 2.61 and 2.62 were produced for both summer and winter conditions.

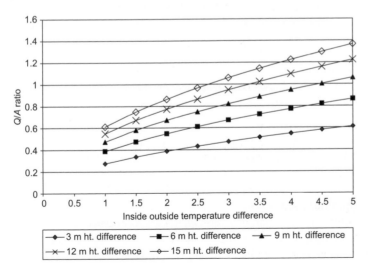

Figure 2.61
Areas of opening required in summer. Volume to area ratio for stack-driven ventilation

Figure 2.62
*Areas of opening
required in winter.
Volume to area ratio for
stack-driven ventilation*

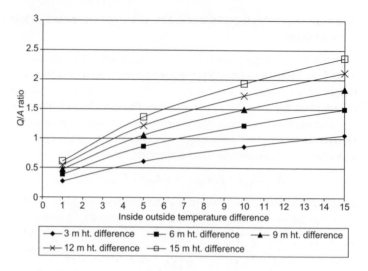

Example of using the graphs

A two-storey building is to be naturally ventilated in both summer and winter and it has been estimated that a volume flow rate of three air changes per hour will be required. Each floor of the building has an area of 500 m² with a slab to slab height of 3 m.

In summer assume that the temperature difference is 4 K and in winter the temperature difference is 10 K. The neutral pressure line is 1 m above the top floor.

Solution

First it is necessary to establish the volume flow rate of air for each floor:

Volume of floor $= 500 \times 3 = 1500\,m^3$
Air change rate $= 3$ per hour
Volume of air supplied $= 1500 \times 3 = 4500\,m^3/hr = 4500/3600$
$$= 1.25\,m^3/s$$

Summer estimation

For the ground floor, assume that the window openings will be 1 m from the ground, which means that they are 6 m from the neutral pressure line. From Fig. 2.61 the Q/A ratio is $0.78\,m^3/s$ per m^2.

The floor area is $1500\,m^3$, therefore the opening area must be:

$$1.25/0.78 = 1.2\,m^2$$

Therefore the windows must have an openable area of at least $1.2\,m^2$ to provide ventilation in summer.

The second floor will need a window opening of $3.5\,m^2$

Winter estimation

The openable areas will be:

$$\text{Ground floor} = 1.25\,m^2$$
$$\text{First floor} = 1.6\,m^2$$

This calculation procedure is a rough approximation but it allows the designer to obtain early on in the design process a rough estimation of the likely areas to be openable. More detailed calculations will be necessary as the design progresses and the complexity of designing for natural ventilation should not be underestimated.

Mixed mode ventilation

Mixed mode ventilation is an increasingly popular system found in buildings with low internal gains and as a supplementary system for naturally ventilated buildings. How does it work? For the majority of the year the building relies on natural ventilation to provide air to the space. If necessary this air is heated by a wet heating system (such as radiators). In hot weather when some cooling may be required the air is extracted from the building via an extract system, usually up the centre of the building (Fig. 2.63). The replacement air enters the building through windows. Usually this outside air will be warm but probably not as warm as the inside air. Therefore, by promoting higher air flows in the space, thermal comfort can be maintained within reasonable tolerances.

This system can also be used at night when cooler outside air is drawn in through the building, cooling the surfaces – particularly the ceilings. With such systems it may well be possible to reduce the peak inside air temperatures during the day by as much as 2–3°C and at night to take advantage of 'free cooling'.

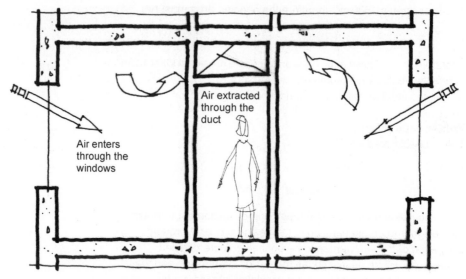

Air extracted through the duct

Air enters through the windows

Figure 2.63 *Example of a mixed mode mechanical ventilation system*

Mechanical ventilation including heat recovery

Mechanical ventilation systems supply and extract air from buildings. They usually incorporate heating and filtration of the air. Also in warm periods they are capable of supplying 100% outside air to the building and when the outside air is cooler than the inside air then this is a source of 'free cooling'.

The transport of air through ductwork (common to mechanical ventilation and full air conditioning systems) is not only space intensive (Fig. 2.64) but can cause noise problems in buildings. To ensure that this is carried out as efficiently as possible make sure that the duct runs are kept simple with bends, contractions and expansions kept to a minimum. This is because every change in direction of air causes a pressure drop which when added up may increase the pressure required by the fan system to 'blow or suck' the air through the system. Bends and other changes in duct sections also create noise which could be a further problem in the building.

It must also be remembered that when ductwork passes through a fire zone then a device known as a fire damper must be fitted.

Figure 2.64 Ceiling voids often become cluttered with services and fans can add to the noise levels within the ducts

In order for the engineers to service and check flow rates it is also necessary to leave access points, and advice should be sought from the engineers before detailing ceiling, wall or floor finishes.

Adequate space should be left for the ductwork and the velocity in the duct kept to about 6 m/s. In Section 3 a simple procedure for estimating the size of the ductwork is given in order that adequate space is left for distribution.

Distribution within rooms

Distribution within the space is also important for the following main reasons:

◆ to remove pollutants
◆ to remove excess heat
◆ to provide fresh air for the occupants
◆ to prevent stagnation which will form a place where fungi could grow.

In meeting these requirements it is easy to create an environment where there is the possibility of having air velocities outside the comfort range for people. One of the challenges of room air distribution design is to avoid draughts around the occupants' feet. In many office developments under-floor plenums are used to deliver air to the space through floor-mounted grilles. These floor-mounted grilles provide fresh conditioned air at low level and at a low velocity. The air rises over the occupants, taking excess heat and moisture with it but surrounding the occupant with conditioned air (Fig. 2.65).

Figure 2.65
Illustration of displacement ventilation

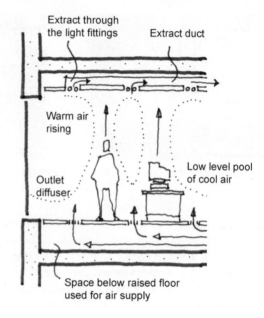

Extract through the light fittings

Extract duct

Warm air rising

Outlet diffuser

Low level pool of cool air

Space below raised floor used for air supply

One advantage of this method of ventilating a building is that it allows for flexibility in the use of the space as the diffusers are easily lifted and repositioned. There are several ways in which air can be delivered to and extracted from a space and Fig. 2.66 shows a range of the most common ways of doing so.

The distribution grilles used in ventilation are themselves capable of altering the direction of the air flow and in some cases capable of adjusting the volumes. The range on the market is very large and a very brief selection of the various types is shown in Fig. 2.67.

Heat recovery systems

Heat recovery from exhaust air is the process of transferring the heat energy in the exhaust air to the supply air. There are a number of possibilities and concepts for heat recovery from exhaust air in both natural and mechanical ventilation. The concept to be chosen depends on the possibilities for utilising the recovered energy. In ordinary mechanical ventilation it is very common to use an air-to-air heat exchanger for direct transfer of heat between exhaust and

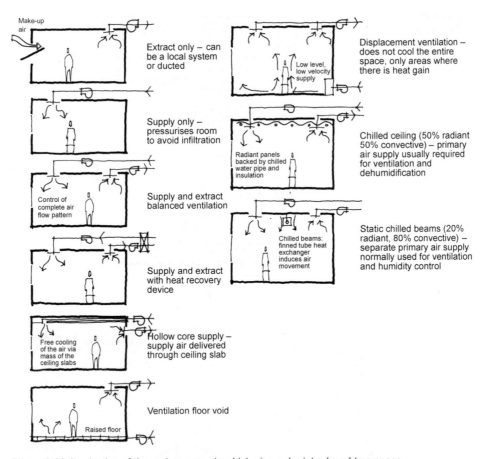

Figure 2.66 A selection of the various ways in which air can be introduced to a space

supply air. In this way, the outdoor air is preheated before it enters the occupied zones in a building.

In naturally ventilated buildings in winter, when the weather is cooler, windows are often left closed and the amount of outside air entering the building can become restricted. In such circumstances it is therefore important to ensure that adequate ventilation is supplied to maintain thermal comfort. Some natural ventilation systems use extract chimneys to remove the air from the building. This, although good in principle, does increase the heating demand

Figure 2.67
A range of air diffusers

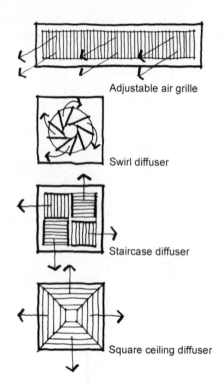

Adjustable air grille

Swirl diffuser

Staircase diffuser

Square ceiling diffuser

Figure 2.68
*A simple heat recovery
system in naturally
ventilated buildings*

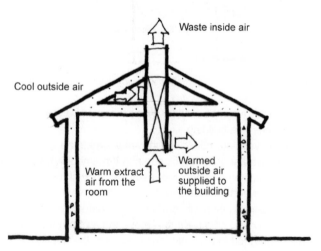

Waste inside air

Cool outside air

Warm extract
air from the
room

Warmed
outside air
supplied to
the building

as the warm air vented to the outside has to be replaced by cooler fresh air which must be heated. In such circumstances it may be possible to use heat recovery to help reduce the energy requirements of the building.

In mechanically ventilated buildings the use of air-to-air heat exchangers requires that supply and exhaust air ducts should to be adjacent to each other, preferably in an air-handling unit. This sometimes imposes restrictions on the layout of the system, especially the ducting system. Figure 2.68 shows a simple heat recovery system for a naturally ventilated building and Fig. 2.69 shows a range of heat recovery possibilities for mechanically ventilated buildings.

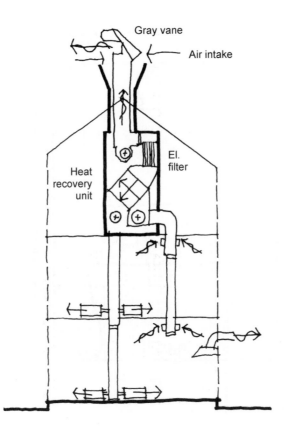

Figure 2.69
A range of heat recovery systems for mechanically ventilated buildings

Air conditioning systems

Full air conditioning

Air conditioning systems are the most complex form of controlling the indoor environment and the building should be designed to minimise their use if at all possible. Figure 2.70 shows the layout of a typical central station air conditioning system.

Such systems are capable of heating, cooling, filtering, mixing outside air with recycled air, humidifying and dehumidifying. To make them work boilers, refrigeration plant and condensers are also needed. All of this equipment takes up valuable space. All of the above processes can be carried out in a single box or split into

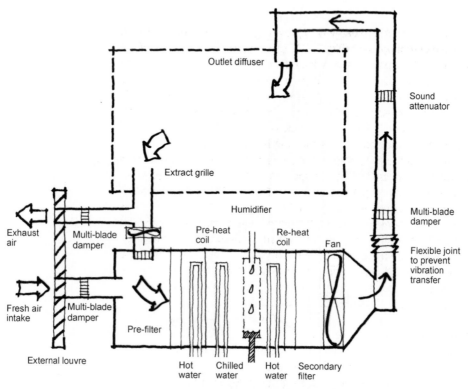

Figure 2.70 *Typical central station air conditioning unit*

Figure 2.71
An example of a roof mounted air conditioning system (note the condenser in the background)

separate parts. A popular way of providing air conditioning is through the use of rooftop plant (Fig. 2.71). These have the advantage of not requiring plant room space inside the building and to some extent the duct space required is less, as the fresh inlet air does not need to be ducted into the plant room, thus saving valuable space. However, it is very easy to assume that all services can be positioned on the roof and it is not long before the roof space begins to look like a jungle of pipes, ducts and boxes. This situation is very easy to fall into, especially at the early stages in the design process, and care should be taken to ensure that the designer is aware of the likely outcome before finalising on plant room space. Figure 2.72 illustrates how a roof space can become cluttered.

If air conditioning is required, the main issues for designers at the concept stage of the design are to ensure that the service runs are simple and adequately provided for in terms of voids, and that plant rooms are provided with appropriate dimensions and suitably located. These simple considerations can be very important in the subsequent detail design.

Partial air conditioning

If parts of the building require air conditioning, steps should be taken to ensure that those areas are adequately isolated from the rest of the building and where possible grouped together to ensure efficiency in distribution. It will then be possible to supply air

Figure 2.72
Roof clutter

conditioning to parts of the building either through ductwork delivering the conditioned air from a central plant or by local plant. Often this type of system uses a direct expansion cooling system where the refrigerant is delivered to the room unit within the space (Fig. 2.73) and the warm refrigerant produced by cooling the room air is condensed in a unit positioned remotely from the room. There are limitations in this type of system due to the length of runs required by the refrigerant lines. Also, if condensation occurs in the room unit, a pipe must be provided to drain the liquid away. There is also a tendency to position the condenser units on the roof of the building (see Figs 2.74 and 2.75) and in some cases they can be a little

Figure 2.73
A typical room unit
from a Direct
Expansion (DX) split
air conditioning system

Figure 2.74
Condenser units on the roof of a building adjacent to a rooftop walkway

Figure 2.75
Retrofit of condenser units on a roof can increase roof clutter

Figure 2.76
Heat exchangers in a hostile coastal environment

unsightly. The efficiency of the operation of such systems can sometimes be a little suspect, particularly if they are positioned in a 'hostile' environment, which can be taken to be in any of our coastal regions where the influence of salt water can cause major problems as shown in Fig. 2.76.

Selecting the appropriate service system at the early stages in the design process is not easy but in Section 3 a range of design options is given which should make the task a little easier. With all service systems it is important that the first considerations are given to making the building envelope as robust as possible.

Artificial lighting

The energy uses in the lighting of buildings can vary between $5\,kWh/m^2$ per year for storage spaces to $60\,kWh/m^2$ per year for an air conditioned office. Lighting costs can be up to 30% of the total utility bill, which is a very significant amount of money. It has been suggested that good lighting design should have an energy rating in the region of $8–12\,W/m^2$. In order to achieve this, careful attention should be given to the provision of lighting at an early stage in the design. The first consideration should be the appropriate provision of

Figure 2.77
*Illustration of a typical
retrofit lighting scheme
where little attention
has been paid to the
varying requirements
of the space*

good quality daylight, followed by the provision of artificial systems
and their control.

The levels and quality of lighting required for a range of functions
have been given in other sections and it therefore only required to
understand how, at the early stages in the design process, provision
for good lighting can be built into the design.

Different functions within a building will require different
approaches and therefore examples for a range of building types
will be explored. Figures 2.77 and 2.78 illustrate only too clearly
how many lighting systems operate – a general array of ceiling-
mounted fittings giving a strong down light on to the working plane
and the natural light from the windows being excluded because it
produces glare on the computer screens. A good design will
address these common faults and produce a working environment
which is both efficient and pleasant to be in. Remembering that the
function of this book is to make designers aware of the many
issues which should be addressed at the early stages in the design
process, general design issues are presented for each building
type selected. No attempt is made to design appropriate lighting
systems. The recommendations given are to be used as aides-
memoires in discussion with either the client or a specialist lighting
designer.

Before investigating the design of lighting systems for a range of building types it is worth understanding the various types of light sources which are available, as the correct choice of lamp and fitting can have a significant effect on the overall performance of the system. In order to rank lamps a term known as the lamp efficacy is used. The efficacy of a lamp is the ratio of the amount of light produced for 1 W of input energy.

Types of lamps found in buildings

There is a wide choice of lamps available on the market and they generally fall into groups depending on how they produce light.

Incandescent sources

Incandescent sources still make up a high percentage of the lighting market as they are cheap to manufacture, give good colour rendering qualities and have a wide range of uses.

The tungsten filament or GLS lamp

In this type of lamp, light is produced by heating a tungsten filament in an inert atmosphere. They tend to have a life of about 1000 hours and the colour rendering properties are good. The lower wattage lamps do tend to produce light in the near red end of the spectrum. The GLS lamp is still a popular choice in many situations because it is cheap to buy and gives a warm colour which is acceptable to many people.

The tungsten halogen lamp

This lamp produces light by heating a tungsten filament in an atmosphere of iodine or bromine which extends the life of the bulb. It has a higher efficacy (up to about 20 Lm/W) than the GLS bulb and generally produces twice the amount of light for twice as long. The colour rendering quality is good and being physically smaller they are good for display lighting.

Gas discharge lamps

These types of sources produce light by passing an electric current through a tube in which mercury or sodium are present along with an inert gas such as krypton or argon. Light is emitted in the ultraviolet (UV) range of the spectrum, and fluorescent coatings are applied to the inside wall of the tube to convert the UV light into visible light. Different combinations of these phosphors produce a wide range in colour rendering properties. These lamps can be either high or low pressure. Such lamps have efficacies in the range of 60–200 Lm/W with a life in the region of 10 000 hours. In order to make these lamps work it is necessary to have a ballast, which is a device to produce a high voltage which 'fires' the lamp. This ballast does take some energy, which lowers the efficacy a little.

Low pressure mercury discharge lamp

As the name implies the tube is partially evacuated and the light is produced by mercury vapour emitting UV light which is then transformed into visible light by the phosphor coating. These lamps have tended to produce a cool light but with the advance in coatings they are now able to produce good colour rendering.

Compact fluorescent lamps (CFL), as the name implies, are physically smaller than the standard fluorescent tube and have efficacies of about 60 Lm/W with a life of about 8000 hours. The control gear for these lamps is usually incorporated within its body, which allows it to be directly placed in fittings designed for GLS lamps. This makes them very competitive with GLS lamps.

Low pressure sodium lamp
As the name implies, sodium is used to produce the light in the tube.
The result is that these lamps give off a yellow light. The efficacy of
this type of lamp is in the region of 120–200 Lm/W. Giving off a yellow
light means that the colour rendering is poor and such lamps are
really only used in external lighting situations, and even there they are
being replaced by other types.

High pressure mercury lamp
The light emitted from this source is both visible and ultraviolet.
The colour rendering can be poor but with a mix of phosphors good
rendering properties can be obtained. The efficacy of these sources
is in the range 40–60 Lm/W.

Metal halide lamps
In addition to the mercury contained in the tube, other elements such
as argon and halide salts (iodides) are used. This mixture of elements
helps to improve the colour rendering properties without the need to
add phosphor coatings to the tube walls. The efficacy of these lamps
is in the region of 70–100 Lm/W.

High pressure sodium
The light emitted by this lamp gives a warm colour and the
efficacy is in the region of 70–130 Lm/W. These lamps tend to be
manufactured in larger wattages, making them more suited to
lighting large areas such as high bay sheds or for exterior
lighting.
    Figure 2.79 shows how the different lamp types perform
against each other. In lighting catalogues it is normal practice to
quote not only the performance of the lamp in terms of its light
output, spectral distribution, and power consumed, but also to
give the Colour Rendering Index. This index is intended to show
how well the lamp responds to the spectral distribution of daylight.
A high index, in the 80s–90s, is regarded as being similar to
daylight, while a low index produces a rather cool blue light.
Another method of identifying the ambience or 'feel' for a lamp
is the colour temperature, which is a measure of the
apparent colour of the light. There are three broad bands for
colour temperature:

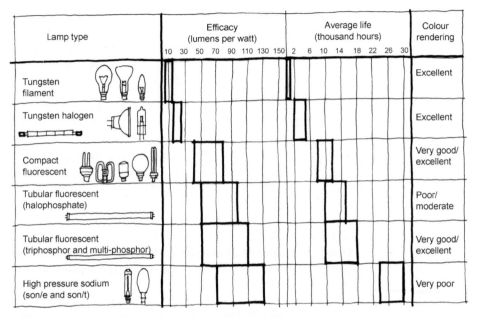

Figure 2.79 *Illustration of the types of lamps used in buildings*

Warm:	below 3300 K
Intermediate:	between 3300 K and 5300 K
Cold:	above 5300 K

Tungsten lamps are generally warm in colour, with high colour temperatures, while fluorescent lighting can be obtained in a range of colour temperatures. In sunlight the colour temperature is in the region of 5500 K, and under bright clear blue skies with snow on the ground the colour temperature can be as high as 10 000 K. At sunrise and dusk the temperature can be about 2000 K.

The lamp holder or luminaire plays a crucial role in distributing the light from the lamp. There are four ways in which light can be distributed from the luminaires (Fig. 2.80):

◆ Upwards – indirect
◆ Downwards in a narrow beam – direct
◆ Evenly distributed between up and down light – diffuse
◆ Partially up and mostly downward – semi-direct.

Figure 2.80
*The four main
distribution types of
luminaires*

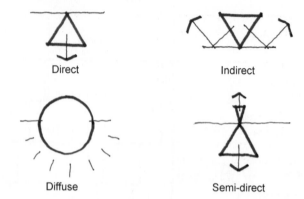

Direct

Indirect

Diffuse

Semi-direct

The choice of which type of fitting to be used can be a complex one and to a great extent the decision will depend on the function taking place in the enclosure. The general characteristics of the four main types of luminaires are set out below.

Direct
These focus the light from the lamp into a narrow beam in a particular direction, which makes them suited to providing direct light on to a surface. However, the surrounding surfaces do not receive much light, which can result in high levels of visual contrast between one surface and another.

Semi-direct
As the name implies, some of the light is directed in a narrow beam – usually downwards – and the rest upwards. This has the effect of distributing some light on to a ceiling, creating bright patches and reducing the visual contrast between surfaces.

Diffuse
Light is distributed in all directions, which gives a very diffuse form of lighting. This is good for illuminating both vertical and horizontal surfaces, and minimising visual contrast between them.

Indirect
In this type of luminaire, the light is directed away from the visual task and normally these are found in situations where good quality

background lighting is required. Applications are in offices where the light is 'bounced' off the ceiling. Depending on the position of these fittings good visual contrast can be obtained.

The design of the luminaire can also affect the efficiency of light distribution and in some cases poorly designed fittings can absorb a significant amount of light which is emitted by the bulb. It is always worth establishing from the manufacturers of luminaires what the efficiency of light distribution actually is. There are cases where, through good design of the luminaire, light losses can be reduced to fractions of one percent while in others the losses can be as much as 20–30%.

General design considerations

It can be seen that designing an effective lighting system early on in the design process can be difficult, as many of the decisions required to inform the design will not have been taken. However, there are several points which can be worked on to ensure that as the design progresses the lighting systems are as efficient as possible.

An important principle of energy efficient lighting design is to ensure that light is directed to where it is required. There is no point lighting a large space to say an overall level of 300 lux when the visual task only takes place infrequently and then only in one corner of the space.

General principles which apply to most buildings can be summarised as follows.

◆ Decide what lighting is really needed, then determine the positions to meet that need.
◆ Use only lamps appropriate to the luminaire.
◆ Ensure that safety lighting is provided.
◆ Try to create some contrast between different surfaces to give effect lighting.
◆ Ensure that there are plenty of switches to allow for switching off those lights that are not needed.
◆ Use automatic control systems where appropriate.

These general principles apply in most buildings but there will be variations and other aspects to be considered in specific types of building. It is therefore helpful to look at the design of lighting for typical building types.

Domestic lighting

In domestic buildings lighting normally only makes up about 5% of the energy consumed, although, being electrical consumption, this translates to about 15% in primary energy terms. However, when viewed from the utility companies' perspective, domestic lighting is a considerable load on the system. For these reasons alone it can be argued that to make savings in the domestic consumption is worthwhile. Unfortunately many householders do not consider it worth making savings or considering design aspects.

Design drivers for lighting of domestic buildings
◆ Ensure that there is plenty of natural light available.
◆ Make provision for adequate outlets for installing stand-alone fittings.
◆ When considering the location of fittings think about the resulting brightness patterns.
◆ Try to specify compact fluorescent lamps for the general lighting of the building, the main reason being that over time they are significantly cheaper to run than equivalent GLS lamps.

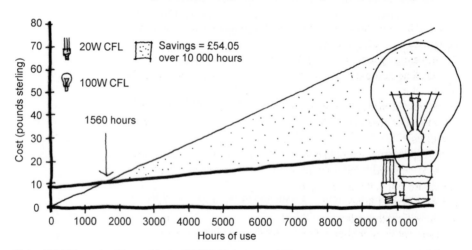

Note: 100 W tungsten filament lamp (GLS) initial output 1330 lumens, cost 50 pence, life hours
20 W compact fluorescent lamp (CFL) initial output 1200 lumens, cost £9.99, life 10 000 hours
cost of electricity 0.0738 pence per unit (kWh)

Figure 2.81 Illustration of the long-term running costs of GLS and CFL

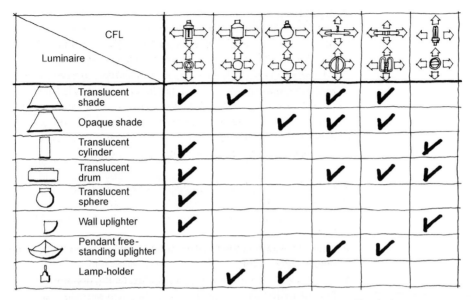

Luminaire / CFL	1	2	3	4	5	6
Translucent shade	✔	✔		✔	✔	
Opaque shade			✔	✔	✔	
Translucent cylinder	✔					✔
Translucent drum	✔			✔	✔	✔
Translucent sphere	✔					
Wall uplighter	✔					✔
Pendant free-standing uplighter				✔	✔	
Lamp-holder		✔	✔			

Figure 2.82 Suitability of compact fluorescent lamps for fitting into a range of luminaires

Figure 2.81 illustrates the difference in running costs over time compared with GLS lamps.

◆ When selecting luminaires try to ensure that they will be suitable for installing compact fluorescent lamps (Fig. 2.82 illustrates this relationship).

◆ Do not use compact fluorescent lamps in situations where there is likely to be frequent switching, e.g. toilets, controlled by movement detectors.

◆ Before specifying dimming controls check that the lamp is capable of being dimmed – fluorescent and some compact fluorescent lamps are not suitable for dimming.

◆ Where compact fluorescent lamps are specified ensure that the fittings for these lamps are not able to accept GLS lamps. This will act as a deterrent to reverting to the less efficient sources.

◆ In spaces where frequent switching takes place it is satisfactory to use GLS lamps as they will not normally be left on for long periods.

◆ Try to keep the use of spotlights to a minimum, although they are good for highlighting specific items such as paintings. They also have a role to play in providing portable reading lights.

◆ For housing estates where there may be a demand for external lighting try to specify high pressure sodium lighting as it is the most efficient source currently available on the mass market.

Industrial buildings

The range of lighting requirements is vast in this sector, ranging from small office environments to very large high bay buildings. In some cases there is a requirement for specialised lighting for inspection tasks. Therefore to deal with this sector can be extremely difficult.

General guidelines for industrial environments are as follows.

◆ Establish as far as possible the range of visual tasks to be carried out in the environment. They may not all be related to the horizontal surface. For example, in storage racks it will be necessary to have good lighting on the vertical plane.

◆ From this analysis determine the optimum lighting levels for the various tasks.

◆ Position luminaires to match the required lighting levels.

◆ Select the appropriate lamp type and luminaire type.

◆ Remember in some applications the light fittings could be positioned in such a way as to make cleaning difficult. To ensure that the lighting system operates efficiently over a period of time it will be necessary to investigate how cleaning can take place.

◆ Install automatic control systems to switch lights off either when there is sufficient natural light or when the space is unoccupied.

◆ In spaces where there is likely to be daylight for a significant part of the working day ensure that the switching is arranged so that the lights are turned off on a grid at right angles to the line of the windows.

Schools

The lighting of schools is a complex issue requiring a great deal of thought. The main priorities in school design are to ensure that the lighting can meet the visual requirements for a range of functions and at the same time meet safety standards. In schools there is a great deal of movement, which adds further complication to the design of lighting systems, which tend to be static.

Classrooms

The main priority is to check that the minimum daylight standards are met and then to design artificial lighting to supplement daylight. If the classroom is to be used in the evening, it will be necessary to design a system which will provide good overall lighting.

General guidelines

◆ Keep the room reflectances high by using light finishes.
◆ Lighting of white boards or copy boards and other vertical surfaces from which students will be required to read must not produce reflections but must have adequate illuminance at the bottom.
◆ Provide overall uniform illuminance to allow for flexibility in room layout.
◆ Consider the use of blackout blinds and dimmer switching of lights to allow data projection or television programmes to be seen without glare from windows or lights.

Laboratories and art rooms

In laboratories it will be necessary not only to have good quality lighting but also colour rendering, and methods for preventing glare or excessive bright patches will be a requirement. For example, in a science laboratory there is the possibility that gas burners could not be seen to be alight if there was direct sunlight falling on the bench – the flame would be invisible.

General guidelines

◆ Where colour rendering is important use fluorescent tubes with colour rendering properties similar to daylight.
◆ The guidelines appropriate to classrooms also apply.
◆ In art rooms it may be necessary to also consider the modelling of the light distribution. Strong down-lighting may accentuate the shadows cast by three-dimensional objects, which may be a visual distraction.

Libraries

These spaces are designed for study and therefore the lighting system should reflect this aspect by providing a calming atmosphere. At the same time it will be necessary to provide good lighting both on the horizontal working plane and vertical book cases. In some cases it may also be necessary to provide some display lighting.

General guidelines

◆ Bookcases should run at right angles to the line of windows.
◆ Use high-reflectance floor finishes – this helps to reflect light upwards towards books stacked at low level.
◆ If possible tilt the bottom shelf towards the direction of light flow.
◆ Locate windows, roof lights and luminaires to illuminate the spines of books rather than horizontal surfaces.
◆ Do not use spotlights to illuminate bookcases.
◆ Up-lighting can be appropriate it the ceiling height is above about 3 m.
◆ Run fluorescent tubes parallel to the line of bookcases and above the walkways.
◆ For normal classroom activities the general issues outlined above also apply.

Assembly and dining halls

These spaces are usually interchangeable and must be able to perform a wide range of tasks – they are truly multifunctional spaces.

General guidelines

◆ Being multifunctional, consider two independent lighting systems – one for general overall lighting for eating, examinations etc. and another with dimming facilities for use when the space is being used as an auditorium.
◆ If the space has a high ceiling and access is good, consider high efficacy discharge lamps in wall mounted up-lighters.
◆ When used as a dining hall consider the colour rendering properties of the lamps, as using lamps with poor rendering properties could make food look unappetising.

Gymnasia

There is a great deal of movement taking place in these spaces and therefore it is necessary to have good quality lighting. Daylight is preferable and to free up wall space consider using clearstory windows.

General guidelines
- ◆ Design for daylight.
- ◆ Consider using high pressure discharge lamps or fluorescent lighting in robust fittings – footballs and other flying objects can cause a great deal of damage in gymnasia.
- ◆ Avoid glare from these fittings.

Offices

Office environments range from small, almost domestic, scale to large open plan volumes. The treatment therefore must be different but the overriding influences must be in providing a lighting environment which allows the occupants to perform their tasks efficiently. With computers forming perhaps the main function in many offices, it is with these in mind that lighting systems have to be designed.

To work effectively in front of a computer screen requires that the lighting system (either natural or artificial) does not produce glare on the screen.

General guidelines
Small offices

- ◆ Provide low levels of background illumination and local task lighting.
- ◆ Use occupancy sensors to switch off lighting when the room is unoccupied.
- ◆ Reduce glare by minimising the luminance differences between different surfaces.
- ◆ Use good colour rendering light sources.

Large offices

- ◆ Similar requirements with respect to glare avoidance as small offices.

◆ Maximise the use of daylight.
◆ Use light coloured surfaces to reflect as much daylight as possible.
◆ Use daylight linked control systems.

Reception areas

◆ Provide good colour rendering sources.
◆ Use highlighting or spots to direct visitors to the desk or assembly point.
◆ Prevent glare on working surfaces.

Sports centres

The wide range of activities which take place within sports centres means that there will be a demand for more than one lighting system. Safety is paramount in these as well as providing aesthetically pleasing spaces. The use of daylight can be an advantage but as most spaces will be internal there may be limited scope to maximise its use. For general spaces such as reception areas or office spaces the lighting should be in accordance with the requirements set out under these sections.

General guidelines
High bay sports halls

◆ If possible integrate daylight with artificial light.
◆ In these spaces the ceiling heights tend to be quite high, which gives the opportunity to use high pressure lamps.
◆ Care to be taken in ensuring that glare is not a problem from these high intensity sources.

Swimming pools

◆ Careful consideration should be given to daylight to prevent glare.
◆ Investigate the use of moisture proof fittings.
◆ Use high pressure lamps.
◆ Consider up-lighting on to ceilings to minimise glare.
◆ Provide sparkle through the use of low voltage halogen lamps.
◆ Ensure that there is no glare on the water surface as this will detract from attendants' ability to monitor swimmers, particularly those swimming under water.

Museums, galleries and libraries

Lighting of these spaces calls for a great deal of thought. In museums there are three possible types of exhibit:

◆ Those that are not sensitive to the actions of UV light – items made of stone, ceramics, metal, glass or enamel fall into this category.
◆ Those that are partially sensitive to the actions of UV light – oil paintings fall into this category as although they contain organic products, there is a degree of protection from the oils in the paint.
◆ Those that are very sensitive to the actions of UV light – items with unprotected organic substances such as drawings, textiles and old manuscripts.

Ultraviolet light is very damaging to items containing organic compounds as it causes fading; both the intensity and time of exposure affect the rate at which fading occurs. It is therefore important to ensure that the amount of damaging UV light is minimised and design procedures put in place to ensure that this does not happen. Coupled with the need to protect displays there is the requirement for allowing users to proceed safely through the galleries, and as a result there could be a conflict in the requirements of the lighting systems.

General guidelines
◆ Use daylight but ensure that it does not fall directly on to the item being displayed. Make sure that the light is bounced at least once off a reflecting surface. Another way to reduce natural UV is to use coatings on the glass to repel the majority of the UV light.
◆ Ensure that the colour rendering index for any lamps used is above 80.
◆ Keep the lux levels as low as possible on the items being displayed but make sure that there is adequate lighting in public spaces.
◆ Avoid highly reflective surfaces as they can contribute to both glare and spectral reflections which could detract from viewing exhibits.

In libraries the main requirement for lighting is to able to read books, papers etc. and therefore the lighting design should reflect this function. Many of the points about libraries have already been outlined in the lighting requirements for schools.

General guidelines
- ◆ Bookcases should run at right angles to the line of windows.
- ◆ Use high-reflectance floor finishes – this helps in reflecting light upwards towards books stacked at low level.
- ◆ If possible tilt the bottom shelf towards the direction of light flow.
- ◆ Locate windows, roof lights and luminaires to illuminate the spines of books rather than horizontal surfaces.
- ◆ Do not use spotlights to illuminate bookcases.
- ◆ Up-lighting can be appropriate if the ceiling height is above about 3 m.
- ◆ Run fluorescent tubes parallel to the line of bookcases and above the walkways.

Theatres

There can be several different lighting schemes in theatres as the functions taking place within them have completely different requirements. No consideration will be given to stage lighting as this is a specialist topic, but it must be remembered that stage lighting can be very intensive on electrical energy usage and therefore provision should be made to ensure that there is sufficient power available.

Some theatres have departments that make costumes and stage sets and in these spaces it is generally required that high quality lighting with very good colour rendering properties is installed. The auditorium itself needs lighting to enable the audience to find their way to and from their seats safely. Outside of performance times, auditorium spaces need to cleaned and maintained, so the lighting scheme must be able to cope with these two functions. Bars, ticket offices and general administration spaces will require general overall lighting with some highlights to provide aesthetic effects. Most of these requirements have already been mentioned, as they are similar to other building types.

General guidelines
Auditorium

- ◆ Sufficient lighting to allow for cleaning could be provided by compact fluorescent tubes (shielded from view).

◆ A lighting system capable of being dimmed – some fluorescent tubes can be dimmed.
◆ Some aesthetic highlighting.
◆ Systems should not produce high levels of contrast between different surfaces.

Foyer bars

◆ Bright exciting aesthetic lighting should be provided in this space.
◆ For daytime use consider daylight.
◆ Glare should be avoided.
◆ Light coloured surfaces to reflect light.

Dressing rooms

◆ Small spaces but good colour rendering properties required.
◆ Bright spaces to ensure that make-up is applied correctly.
◆ System should be capable of being reduced in level to enable the actor/actress to relax.

Costume and scenery manufacturing workshops

◆ High levels of light with good colour rendering properties.
◆ Glare minimised by ensuring that surfaces are light in colour and are diffusing.
◆ Similar requirements to those in school art rooms.
◆ Provision for portable lighting to reach awkward spaces.

Hospitals

These buildings must accommodate several different lighting systems. Part of their operations is similar to general office environments, some related to foyer spaces and others more specialised. Patients can be stimulated by bright, aesthetic, pleasing environments and lighting can be a major contributor to this feeling of well-being.

General guidelines
Office spaces

◆ The same principles as already set out apply.

Reception spaces

◆ Lighting must be appropriate for the staff to deal with records – general horizontal illuminance requirements should be met.
◆ Glare should be avoided on computer screens.
◆ Bright pleasant lighting should be provided for the patients.

Wards

◆ Provide daylight.
◆ Ensure that surface finishes are able to reflect as much daylight as possible.
◆ Overall good lighting of horizontal surfaces should be met with the possibility of dimming the levels.
◆ Avoid glare.
◆ Many patients will be in bed and therefore high brightness patches from light fittings should be avoided.
◆ Provide local lighting to each bed space.
◆ Use lamps with a high colour rendering index.

Treatment rooms

◆ Avoid strong shadows by using diffusing fittings.
◆ Use lamps with a high colour rendering index.
◆ Avoid specular reflections by using matt or semi-matt surface finishes.

Operating theatres

These are highly specialised areas requiring extremely high levels of light as well as good colour rendering index lamps. The design of lighting systems for these spaces should be left to specialists in this field and their advice implemented.

Retail sector

Generally, shops require a lighting system which advertises the products on sale. To do so effectively requires lamps with a high colour rendering index and the use of spots to highlight the products.

Lighting costs in this sector can range from 20 to 70% of the overall energy cost and therefore it is important to reach a balance between the requirements of the lighting system and energy usage.

General guidelines
◆ High level of general lighting.
◆ Ability to alter the layout of spot lighting and other display lighting.
◆ Provide plenty of 'sparkle'.
◆ Use lamps with a high colour rendering index.
◆ Where space allows, consider using high pressure lamps in upward diffusing fittings – this will help in reducing what is generally regarded as high energy use.
◆ Use daylight linking when possible – when there is sufficient daylight the unnecessary lights are automatically switched off.
◆ Use localised switching to give lower levels during cleaning and restocking periods.
◆ Investigate the use of different lighting levels to identify routes through large retail outlets – for example virtual corridors could be defined by using lower levels of light than in the display areas.
◆ Use contrast effects to define building layout.

Places of worship

In many respects the function of these spaces maps very well on to the requirements for theatres in that there will be many occasions where the congregation or 'audience' will require general reading lighting but the main function will be to watch the clergy or choir. This sector is not particularly large in terms of new building but there is plenty of opportunity to produce good quality lighting in refurbishment projects. The lighting quality in many churches could be regarded as being poor and in need of 'bringing up to date'.

General guidelines
◆ If possible make the best use of daylight.
◆ Ensure that the paint finishes reflect light – particularly ceilings. There are still many dark cream or other poorly reflecting finishes around.
◆ Replace GLS with compact fluorescent lamps.
◆ Try to use diffusing light.
◆ If possible use high pressure discharge lamps provided that they can be placed in fittings which are diffusing.
◆ Localised highlighting of particular areas should be provided.

◆ Provide localised switching to allow for cleaning and maintenance in one part of the building to be carried out effectively without the need to light the whole premises.
◆ Ensure that the lighting of the pulpit or other space higher than the congregation does not cause glare.

Lighting controls

In many applications it has been stressed that the use of daylight should be the first consideration, strongly followed by a need to ensure that the selected lighting scheme can be adequately controlled. In common with the heating energy usage of a building, the effectiveness of a lighting scheme can depend on the ability to control when the lights are switched on.

The main methods of providing control to a lighting scheme are:

◆ Time switching – carried out by a time clock which simply allows the lights to be switched on during specific periods of time.
◆ Localised switching – either individual switches or connected to a group of lights. When connected to a group of lights it is important to ensure that the group adequately reflects the user pattern.
◆ Occupancy linking – these are controllers which detect movement and when the space is empty the lights are switched off.
◆ Photoelectric daylight linking – this method will only allow lights to be switched on when there is not sufficient daylight.

Each of these systems has a positive role to play in the design of an effective lighting system and Fig. 2.83 illustrates one way of choosing the most appropriate control system.

Refurbishment

In refurbishment projects the above considerations should be analysed because often, looking at how the scheme could be designed will highlight a way forward.

General guidelines
Initially there may be cost constraints on the ability to completely replace the whole system and therefore it will be necessary to look at improving the system in stages. The first thing to note about old

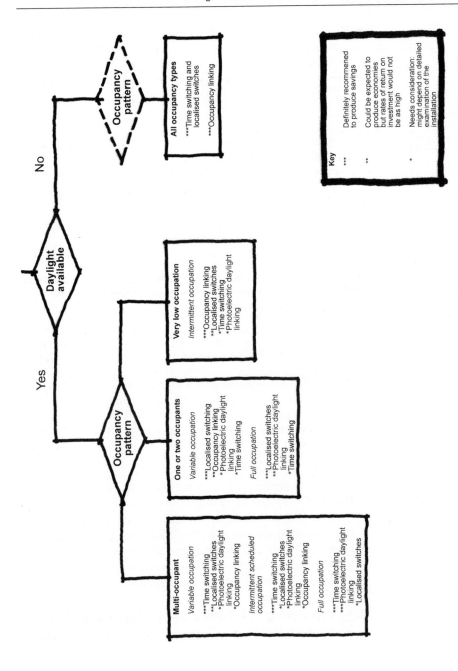

Figure 2.83 *Flowchart to help select the most appropriate lighting control strategies (Source: Energy Efficient Lighting in Offices, Thermie Programme Action, Commission of the European Communities, BRE, Watford.)*

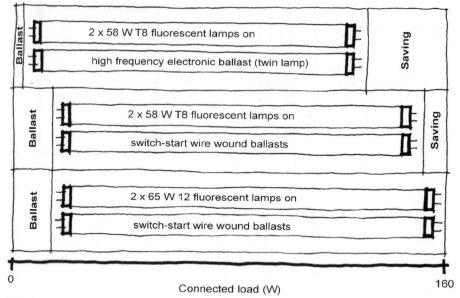

Note Lamps operate at 50 W on high frequency electronic ballasts

Figure 2.84 Energy characteristics of fluorescent tubes

systems is that it is quite possible that the layout of the fittings is satisfactory but the choice of lamp/fitting combination may be absorbing a disproportionate amount of the available light and therefore this is the place to start investigating.

- Make sure that the windows are clean/clear to allow available daylight to be used.
- Consider replacing old fluorescent tubes with new tubes (Fig. 2.84 illustrates the energy saving benefits).
- Replace GLS lamps with compact fluorescent lamps.
- Replace old fittings with new fittings (often the existing fittings will have a plastic diffuser over the lamp which will be faded and therefore will be absorbing up to 60% of the available light).
- Consider re-switching existing circuits to allow for better control of when lights are on.
- Investigate the use of stand-alone up-lighters to supplement existing fixed lamps.

Section 3

Aids at design stage to help
produce an energy efficient
building

Energy

In this section general rules of thumb are given to help you to formulate the building shape, location and space allocation for services. This is an essential part of design, particularly at the early stages in the design process as, by getting the form and layout approximately right, time (and also money) will be saved later on in the project.

The main issues, which are of importance when designing an energy efficient building are

◆ the flexibility of the brief
◆ site analysis
◆ fabric design with respect to heat gains/losses, thermal mass
◆ provision of appropriate service space
◆ type of control systems to be used and operational programmes
◆ environmental strategy.

Having considered the above issues it is then possible to have in principle a building design which will be energy efficient. However, as the design firms up it will probably be necessary for some of the issues to be explored in more detail by the environmental consultants. This process will not only firm up on the detail design but also should not normally require major alterations to your design, as having considered them early on in the design process you will have allocated space or defined particular aspects to deal with the stated requirements.

Flexibility of the brief

To a large extent this is dictated by the user requirements. It may be able to persuade the client to be more relaxed about the environmental performance of the building if it can be demonstrated that the benefits of doing so will result in lower energy costs or the building will be more sustainable. Much of what the client is told is contained in the various sections in this book and debates over the precise form of the brief must be developed to suit the particular situation. Confidence in the brief will be enhanced if it is possible to quote from existing buildings which have been able to demonstrate successes in either energy or environmental performance.

Site analysis

Before carrying out a site analysis it is necessary to establish the priorities. For example, if the site is in the middle of a city then the scope to deal with solar access will be severely limited due to the surrounding buildings and it may therefore not be possible to do much about it. However, on a greenfield site there will be more scope to maximise solar access.

A site analysis dealing with environmental issues should take into consideration the following points:

◆ solar access
◆ local wind environment
◆ availability of daylight
◆ sources of local pollutants
◆ local noise environment.

Solar access
Good solar access is important if the building is to make use of the sun's energy to help in producing a passively heated building. As mentioned previously, by keeping the south elevation free from obstructions, solar access is possible. The simple rule governing layout of buildings to maximise the benefits of sunlight is demonstrated opposite and in Fig. 3.1 on p. 152.

Design pointer – solar access

Flat sites

Obstruction

α = Critical angle in deg.

Period of year	London–Bristol	Liverpool–Manchester	Glasgow–Edinburgh	Other location (latitude)
All year	13	11	9	65°
21 Jan – 21 Nov	17	15	12	68°
6 Feb – 6 Nov	21	19	16	72°
21 Feb – 21 Oct	27	25	22	78°

Sloping sites

Window reference line

Wind effects

Wind shelter

Wind shelter can be provided by several means – other buildings, natural vegetation or artificial wind breaks. The prevailing wind in the UK comes from the south west and it is normal to consider this direction first when dealing with shelter. However, it must also be remembered that in winter strong cold northerly winds can be experienced which can cause a problem not only with speed – producing extra wind-chill, driving rain and less frequently driving snow. Local libraries or information centres sometimes hold information on local climate.

Providing wind shelter may also be in conflict with the desire to provide solar access – particularly to the southwest.

Design pointer – wind shelter

For passive solar buildings facing south with planted shelter to the south and west, good solar access for winter sun is maintained if the shelter is at least four times the height of the building distant from it for latitudes up to 55°N and five times the height of the building distant up to 60°N.

The north façade of buildings still require daylight so a shelter belt on the north side should be at least twice the height of the building away.

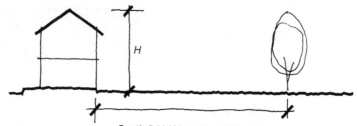

South 5 *H*, West 4 *H*, North 2 *H*

Shelter belts at the edge of an estate or groups of buildings should be about 2 *H* to protect daylight availability (although some sunlight will be sacrificed).

Shelter belts protecting open spaces will be effective at reducing wind speed by the following amounts.

Distance from belt in belt height (*H*)	% Reduction in wind speed
2	60
5	40
10	20
15	10

Wind turbulence around buildings
When carrying out a survey of a site make sure that the layout of other buildings is considered in some detail. The layout of the surrounding

buildings may be such that it is possible for them to act as barriers, diverting the flows into narrower areas and causing strong local wind effects.

Design pointer – wind effects

Strong winds can be generated by air dropping down the façade

Winds being channelled between buildings

Strong winds around edges of buildings

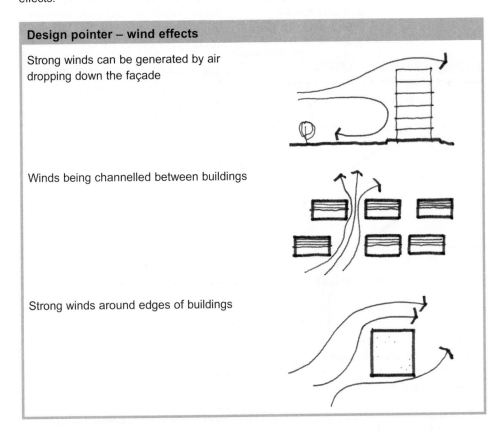

Effect of plants

Planting can have a significant effect on the environment of an area, particularly by providing privacy, solar shading and wind shelter. The effectiveness of a shelter belt has been set out in Section 2 but in general terms a belt can be expected to give some shelter when the distance from the belt is up to about 10 to 15 times its height. Natural shelter belts are better than solid belts because they allow some air to pass through, which enhances their performance as they avoid a rapid change in the wind gradient from the ground upwards.

Daylight availability
The availability of daylight is dependent on the density and height of the surrounding buildings and in a site analysis it would be advisable to ascertain the relative heights and distances between buildings.

Design pointers – daylight

If it is desired to let the internal spaces be daylit, it is first necessary to establish the desired Daylight Factor.

- From Section 2 it was established that daylight factors between 2 and 5% would be desirable.
- If a window is to be used for providing daylight then obstructions should not be higher than 25° above the horizon (Fig. 3.1)

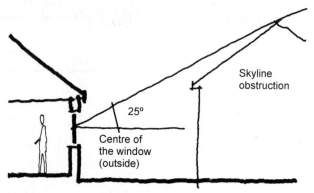

Figure 3.1 *Limit of obstructions for daylight availability*

- A room can have a daylit appearance if the area of the glazing is at least 1/25th of the total room area.
- Areas of a room from which there is no direct view of the sky are likely to have a low level of daylight (Fig. 3.2).
- Surfaces that are closer to a window than twice the height of the window head above desktop level are likely to receive adequate daylight for most of the working year.
- Using the graphs shown in Fig. 3.3 it is possible to establish the likely percentage of the year when daylight would be adequate for defined levels of illuminance. Normal conditions of clear or tinted glass, light interiors and working day 9 a.m. to 5 p.m. were assumed for these graphs.

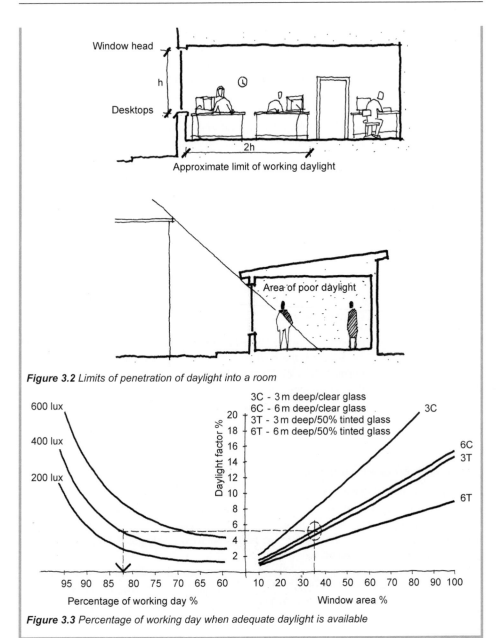

Figure 3.2 Limits of penetration of daylight into a room

Figure 3.3 Percentage of working day when adequate daylight is available

Sources of pollutants

During a site survey it is advisable to look for any sources of pollutants which may impinge on the proposed building/s. Such sources could be industrial emissions, extracts of waste air from mechanically ventilated buildings and traffic flows. Notes should be kept of the locality of these emissions and steps taken to find out about their intensity and frequency. Quite often local authorities have information on local emissions which can be helpful.

Design pointers – emissions

- Establish locality, frequency and content
- Indicate their position and possible path across the site (local wind data will help in determining this).

Fabric design

Having determined whether the site climate will affect the design of the building, the next stage is to investigate the fabric design of the building. Section 2 contains information related to this issue but at the initial stages of the design process it is more important to consider how the mass of the building will affect the energy requirements.

Design pointers – building shape

- Narrow buildings use less energy in total as they can be more effectively daylit and this leads to a reduction in electrical load. This outweighs any slight increase in fabric losses due to a large façade area.
- Courtyard buildings do not perform as well as shallow buildings as they have less daylight and natural ventilation.
- Atrium buildings perform in a similar way to courtyard buildings, although the ventilation is better than courtyard (due to stack effects). There may be a need to have mechanical ventilation to the upper floors due to the low stack pressures at higher levels.

Design pointers – glazing ratio

- Buildings with very small glazing ratios will use significantly more energy than buildings with larger glazing ratios.
- Increasing glazing ratios much above about 50% will produce little extra benefit.
- The optimum glazing ratio is in the region of 30–50% for vertical surfaces.
- The optimum glazing ratio for roof-light is no more than 20%.
- Before finalising glazing ratios do a check on overheating potential.

Overheating

At the initial stages in the design process it is difficult to determine exactly by how much a space may overheat. The quick calculation given in Section 2 with respect to the current

Table 3.1 Lightweight building up to 6 m deep, room height 2.4 m

Glazing ratio (%)	Double glazing		Double low e		Tinted	
	T_{max} with internal shading	T_{max} with external or mid-pane shading	T_{max} with internal shading	T_{max} with external or mid-pane shading	T_{max} with internal shading	T_{max} with external or mid-pane shading
40	29	28	29	28	28	28
60	29	27	29	27	28	27
80	29	27	29	27	28	27
100	30	27	29	27	28	27

Table 3.2 Lightweight building up to 6 m deep, room height 2.7–3 m

Glazing ratio (%)	Double glazing		Double low e		Tinted	
	T_{max} with internal shading	T_{max} with external or mid-pane shading	T_{max} with internal shading	T_{max} with external or mid-pane shading	T_{max} with internal shading	T_{max} with external or mid-pane shading
40	29	27	28	27	27	27
60	29	26	28	27	27	26
80	29	26	28	28	28	26
100	29	26	29	29	28	26

Building Regulations Part L2 will give a very rough estimate. Another way of reaching a quick conclusion with respect to determining the likelihood of overheating occurring is to make an estimate based on the work of the Building Research Establishment's procedure for naturally ventilated and daylit offices. See Tables 3.1–3.4. This procedure is based on computer simulations for a range of specific design parameters and then correction factors are applied to take into account variations from the standard. A summary of this work is presented in Table 3.5 and the correction factors for different situations in Table 3.6.

Table 3.3 Lightweight building 6 to 8 m deep, room height 2.4 m

Glazing ratio (%)	Double glazing		Double low e		Tinted	
	T_{max} with internal shading	T_{max} with external or mid-pane shading	T_{max} with internal shading	T_{max} with external or mid-pane shading	T_{max} with internal shading	T_{max} with external or mid-pane shading
40	30	28	29	28	29	28
60	29	28	29	28	28	28
80	29	27	29	27	28	27
100	30	27	29	27	28	27

Table 3.4 Lightweight building 6 to 8 m deep, room height 2.7 to 3 m

Glazing ratio (%)	Double glazing		Double low e		Tinted	
	T_{max} with internal shading	T_{max} with external or mid-pane shading	T_{max} with internal shading	T_{max} with external or mid-pane shading	T_{max} with internal shading	T_{max} with external or mid-pane shading
40	29	27	28	27	28	27
60	29	27	28	27	28	27
80	29	26	28	27	28	26
100	29	26	29	26	28	26

Table 3.5 *Temperatures and subjective response*

Maximum temperature (°C)	Subjective rating	People possibly dissatisfied (%)
26	Good	10
27	Tolerable	20–25
28	Poor	<30
29	Unacceptable	>30

Table 3.6 *Initial estimation using internal blinds*

Corrections	London	Aberdeen
Initial temperature	29	29
Heavyweight building	0	0
Region	0	−2
Location	0	−2
Orientation	0	0
Internal gains	+1	+1
Early morning cooling	0	0
Window openable area	−1	−1
Ventilation strategy	−1	−1
Final temperature	28	24

Corrections
Heavyweight buildings: −1°C

Region
South and West England and Wales   0°C
North of England, Ireland and North Wales   −1°C
For Scotland   −2°C

Location
Urban   0°C
Rural   −1°C
Coastal   −2°C

Orientation
SSE–WNW   0°C
WNW–NWN and NNE–SSE   −1°C
NNW–NNE   −2°C

Internal gains

15 W/m^2	0°C
25 W/m^2	+1°C
35 W/m^2	+2°C

Early morning cooling (for heavyweight)   −1°C

Window openable area

Up to 30%	+1°C
30–50%	0°C
50–100%	−1°C

Ventilation strategy

Single sided	0°C
Double sided	−1°C

The tables produce a temperature figure and the interpretation of this figure is given in Table 3.4.

Example

It is intended to construct two identical office blocks for a client, one in London and one in Aberdeen. They are to have 40% double glazing on the south elevation with an opening area of 75%. The buildings are initially designed to be lightweight with a ceiling height of 2.4 m and a depth of 6m with cross ventilation. The internal gains are predicted to be 25 W/m^2. The client wishes to know what combination of thermal mass and shading is to be used to minimise the potential for overheating.

Result

The building in London will have an internal temperature of 28°C, which means that there will be a poor internal environment resulting in between 25 and 30% of the occupants being dissatisfied. The building in Aberdeen with 24°C should produce a good internal environment.

Measures which could be taken in the London development include:

Making the building heavyweight	−1°C
Early morning cooling	−1°C
Reducing the internal gains to 15 W/m^2	−1°C

Using external shading   −1°C
Increasing the ceiling height to 3 m   −1°C

The possible total reductions are 5°C, which would give an internal temperature of 24°C, which is the same as Aberdeen.

Another way of estimating the possibility of overheating is to use the simplified computer program LT for Europe developed by a team of international experts and coordinated by the Martin Centre at the University of Cambridge. This procedure not only shows the breakdown in energy usage between heating, lighting and cooling but also gives an estimate of the number of overheating periods in a year that a particular room will experience. Figures 3.4 and 3.5 show screens from this program.

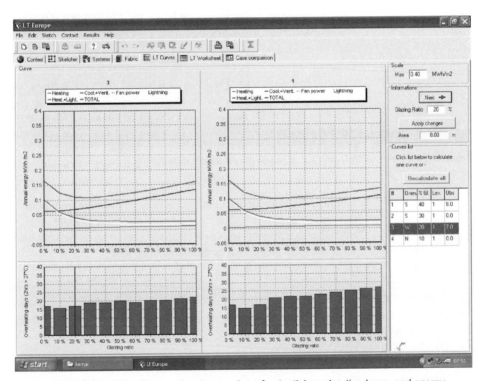

Figure 3.4 *Output of LT for Europe showing number of potential overheating hours and energy consumption curves*

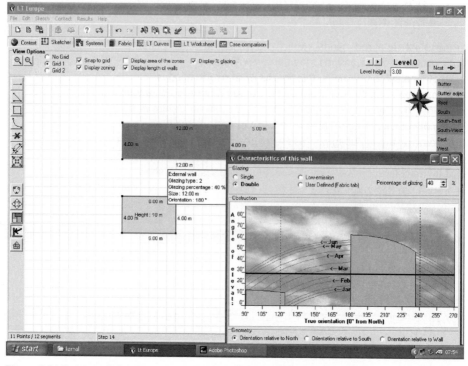

Figure 3.5 *LT plan and view from south elevation of a simple building*

It must be remembered that this is only an estimate and more detailed calculations will be necessary to establish the real overheating potential. These calculations should be carried out using recognised software by a competent consultant.

Design pointers – overheating

- Use either the tables or the Building Regulations procedure to establish if overheating could be an issue.
- Use the tables to adjust the design.
- If available use the LT for Europe program to determine overheating hours and glazing ratios.

Estimating the amount of thermal mass to include in the building

In Section 2 we introduced the topic of thermal mass and demonstrated that using mass to absorb heat gains could reduce the peak internal air temperatures. To obtain an accurate estimate of the amount to be used it is really necessary to use one of the advanced computer simulation models. However, the procedure set out below is aimed at establishing the appropriate amount to be included at the early design stages. Although this procedure seems simple to use, it is actually quite accurate as the case study in Section 5 on the Gasser office block in Chur, Switzerland, demonstrates. The amount of thermal mass in this building was established by using a very similar approach to that set out below, and by using this the same amount of mass was suggested. The Gasser building does work, so there is some confidence in using this procedure.

Step 1. Determine the solar gains
Find the likely solar gains for the space. Computer simulations can be carried out to determine exactly the likely solar gain, but as we are trying to establish ballpark figures, it is sufficient to use the data given in Table 3.7.

Table 3.7 Solar gains for different regions in the UK in MJoules

Scotland

	N	NW	W	SW	S	SE	E	NE
January	0.9	0.9	1.3	2.3	2.9	2.3	1.3	0.9
February	2	2.1	2.8	4.4	5.3	4.4	2.8	2.1
March	3.4	3.6	4.6	6	6.9	6	4.6	3.6
April	5.3	6	7.4	8.9	9.5	8.9	7.4	6
May	7.1	8.1	9.8	10.7	10.7	10.7	9.8	8.1
June	7.7	8.5	9.7	10.1	10	10.1	9.7	8.5
July	7.4	8.4	9.6	10.2	10.1	10.2	9.6	8.4
August	5.9	6.6	7.9	8.9	9.3	8.9	7.9	6.6
September	4.1	4.4	5.8	7.3	8	7.3	5.8	4.4
October	2.3	2.4	3.1	4.5	5.3	4.5	3.1	2.4
November	1.2	1.2	1.7	2.9	3.7	2.9	1.7	1.2
December	0.7	0.7	0.8	1.5	2	1.5	0.8	0.7

Table 3.7 Continued

North England

	N	NW	W	SW	S	SE	E	NE
January	1.2	1.2	1.4	2.2	2.7	2.2	1.4	1.2
February	2.1	2.1	2.5	3.5	3.9	3.5	2.5	2.1
March	3.6	3.7	4.6	5.9	6.6	5.9	4.6	3.7
April	5.3	5.8	6.8	7.9	8.3	7.9	6.8	5.8
May	7	7.9	9.3	10	10	10	9.3	7.9
June	7.8	8.8	10.1	10.4	10.2	10.4	10.1	8.8
July	7.4	8.4	9.6	10.1	10	10.1	9.6	8.4
August	5.9	6.6	7.9	8.8	9.1	8.8	7.9	6.6
September	4.2	4.6	5.6	7	7.7	7	5.6	4.6
October	2.6	2.7	3.4	4.8	5.5	4.8	3.4	2.7
November	1.3	1.4	1.9	3.1	3.7	3.1	1.9	1.4
December	0.9	0.9	1.2	2.2	2.7	2.2	1.2	0.9

Mid England and North Wales

	N	NW	W	SW	S	SE	E	NE
January	1.2	1.2	1.6	2.8	3.5	2.8	1.6	1.2
February	2.1	2.1	2.9	4.4	5.3	4.4	2.9	2.1
March	3.3	3.5	4.5	5.8	6.6	5.8	4.5	3.5
April	5	5.8	7.3	8.6	9.1	8.6	7.3	5.8
May	6.4	7.4	8.9	9.6	9.5	9.6	8.9	7.4
June	7	7.9	9.2	9.6	9.2	9.6	9.2	7.9
July	6.7	7.7	9.1	9.5	9.3	9.5	9.1	7.7
August	5.6	6.5	8.1	9.2	9.4	9.2	8.1	6.5
September	4	4.4	5.9	7.4	8.2	7.4	5.9	4.4
October	2.3	2.4	3.4	4.9	5.8	4.9	3.4	2.4
November	1.3	1.4	2	3.6	4.4	3.6	2	1.4
December	0.8	0.8	1.2	2.2	2.8	2.2	1.2	0.8

Table 3.7 Continued

South England

	N	NW	W	SW	S	SE	E	NE
January	1.2	1.2	1.6	2.8	3.5	2.8	1.6	1.2
February	2.1	2.1	2.9	4.3	5.1	4.3	2.9	2.1
March	3.4	3.7	5	6.5	7.4	6.5	5	3.7
April	5	5.8	7.2	8.5	8.9	8.5	7.2	5.8
May	6.5	7.5	9.2	9.9	9.8	9.9	9.2	7.5
June	7.2	8.4	9.8	10.2	9.7	10.2	9.8	8.4
July	6.9	7.9	9.3	9.8	9.5	9.8	9.3	7.9
August	5.7	6.6	8.2	9.3	9.5	9.3	8.2	6.6
September	4.1	4.7	6.2	8	8.9	8	6.2	4.7
October	2.6	2.7	3.8	5.7	6.7	5.7	3.8	2.7
November	1.4	1.4	2	3.5	4.3	3.5	2	1.4
December	0.9	0.9	1.2	2.2	2.7	2.2	1.2	0.9

Southwest England and South Wales

	N	NW	W	SW	S	SE	E	NE
January	1.3	1.3	1.7	2.9	3.6	2.9	1.7	1.3
February	2.3	2.4	3.3	5.2	6.3	5.2	3.3	2.4
March	3.6	3.9	5.5	7.2	8.2	7.2	5.5	3.9
April	5.3	6.2	8.3	10	10.4	10	8.3	6.2
May	6.9	8.2	10.2	11	10.8	11	10.2	8.2
June	7.6	8.9	10.7	10.9	10.4	10.9	10.7	8.9
July	7.1	8.4	10.1	10.6	10.2	10.6	10.1	8.4
August	5.8	6.9	8.7	9.9	10	9.9	8.7	6.9
September	4.3	4.9	6.6	8.5	9.5	8.5	6.6	4.9
October	2.7	2.8	3.8	5.5	6.5	5.5	3.8	2.8
November	1.6	1.6	2.3	3.8	4.8	3.8	2.3	1.6
December	1	1	1.5	2.7	3.4	2.7	1.5	1

These figures take no account of any solar shading which may be present and such shading will obviously affect the total amount of energy transmitted to the inside. To simplify the calculations it is suggested that the correction factors given in Table 3.8 are used.

Table 3.8 *Correction factors for solar gain through glazing (derived from CIBSE Guide Book A: Solar Transmission Factors)*

	Solar correction factor
No blinds, double glass	1
Double glass, external shading	0.17
Double glass, mid-pane shading	0.42
Double glass, internal shading	0.67
Double glass, tinted or reflecting glass	0.43
For triple glass subtract from correction	0.03

Step 1. For each elevation establish the solar gain and multiply this by both the area of glass and the shading factor.

Solar

	Gain MJ		Window area		Solar correction		Total MJ
North		×		×		=	Box 1
Northeast		×		×		=	Box 2
East		×		×		=	Box 3
Southeast		×		×		=	Box 4
South		×		×		=	Box 5
Southwest		×		×		=	Box 6
West		×		×		=	Box 7
Northwest		×		×		=	Box 8
TOTAL							Box 9 = Sum Boxes 1–8

Step 2. Establish the internal gains and complete the calculation chart below:

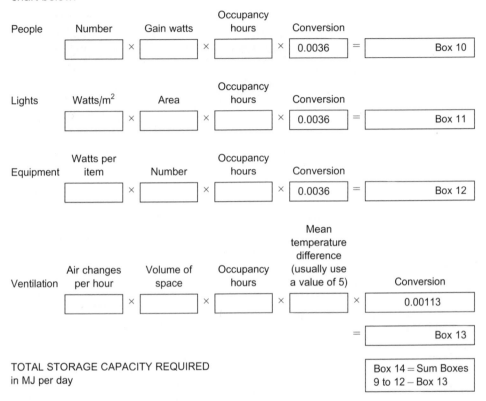

People Number × Gain watts × Occupancy hours × Conversion 0.0036 = Box 10

Lights Watts/m² × Area × Occupancy hours × Conversion 0.0036 = Box 11

Equipment Watts per item × Number × Occupancy hours × Conversion 0.0036 = Box 12

Ventilation Air changes per hour × Volume of space × Occupancy hours × Mean temperature difference (usually use a value of 5) × Conversion 0.00113

= Box 13

TOTAL STORAGE CAPACITY REQUIRED in MJ per day

Box 14 = Sum Boxes 9 to 12 – Box 13

(For heat gains from people it is good enough to use 140 W per person)

Step 3. Establish areas available for storage

Area to be used for storage		% stored in element		Storage required kJ/m² K
Walls	Box 15 m²	Box 19 = Box 15/Box 18	Box 22 = Box 14 × Box 19	Box 22 × 1000/ Box 15
Ceiling	Box 16 m²	Box 20 = Box 16/Box 18	Box 23 = Box 14 × Box 20	Box 23 × 1000/ Box 16
Floor	Box 17 m²	Box 21 = Box 17/Box 18	Box 24 = Box 14 × Box 21	Box 24 × 1000/ Box 17
Total	Box 18 = Box 15 + Box 16 + Box 17			

Use the value in kJ/m² to establish the type of material, thickness and temperature rise from Figs 3.6 to 3.9. Select a material and thickness from the graphs and, working backwards, establish the possible storage capacity and then compare this capacity with the requirement.

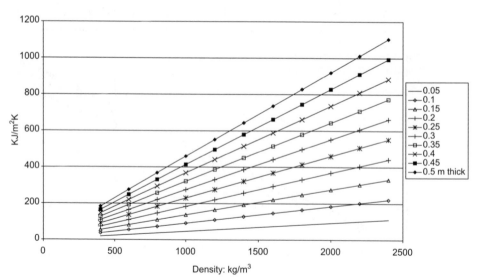

Figure 3.6 Heat capacity of concrete for different thicknesses and for unit area

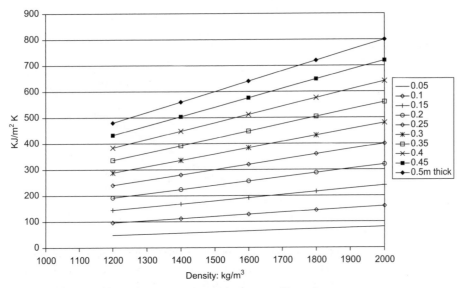

Figure 3.7 *Heat capacity of brick for different thicknesses and for unit area*

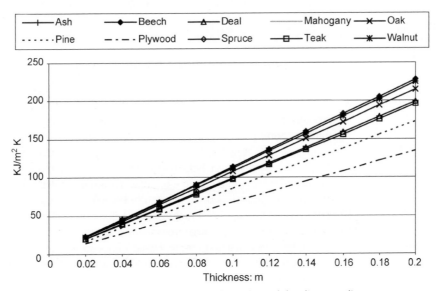

Figure 3.8 *Heat capacity of timbers for varying thicknesses and density per unit area*

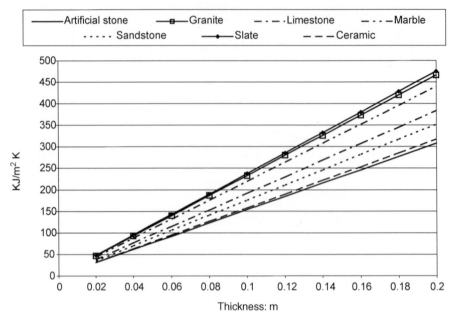

Figure 3.9 *Heat capacity of stones for varying thicknesses and density per unit area*

Where can thermal mass be used?

Thermal mass can be used anywhere in a building but the most effective locations are those where it is easy to absorb heat. Exposed ceilings are perhaps the best location as warm air rises and can therefore easily be absorbed into the surface. Also, a warm ceiling (in winter) will help to keep the radiant temperature slightly higher, which will help in promoting thermal comfort. The removal of heat from a ceiling can either be through passing cooler air over the surfaces (above, through or below) or by passing cooled water through the structure. There is no one solution to the position of or removal of heat from thermal mass – each application is specific to that building. Vertical walls can also be used but these can be covered in decorations or paintings, which will detract from their effectiveness.

Example of using this procedure

An office building in northern England has the following conditions:

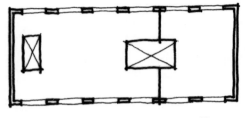

Length $= 50\,$m
Width $= 10\,$m
Storey height $= 3\,$m

N

S

Glass area on the south façade is $45\,\text{m}^2$ double glazing with external blinds.

Occupancy 10 people for 6 hours per day doing office work
Lighting load $12\,\text{W/m}^2$ and switched on for 2 hours per day
Equipment load $30\,\text{W/m}^2$

Ventilation rate is estimated to be 1 air change per hour

Estimate the amount of thermal mass to deal with the projected loads in July. Assume that the structure will gain 1°C in temperature rise over the day.

Solution

Step 1. Establish solar gains through windows
From Table 3.8 for south-facing windows the daily heat gain is
10.2 MJ. The worksheet can now be completed.

Solar

	Gain MJ		Window area		Solar correction		Total MJ
North		×		×		=	Box 1
Northeast		×		×		=	Box 2
East		×		×		=	Box 3
Southeast		×		×		=	Box 4
South	10.2	×	45	×	0.17	=	78.03 Box 5
Southwest		×		×		=	Box 6
West		×		×		=	Box 7
Northwest		×		×		=	Box 8

TOTAL

78.03
Box 9 = Sum Boxes 1–8

Step 2. Establish the internal gains and complete the calculation chart below:

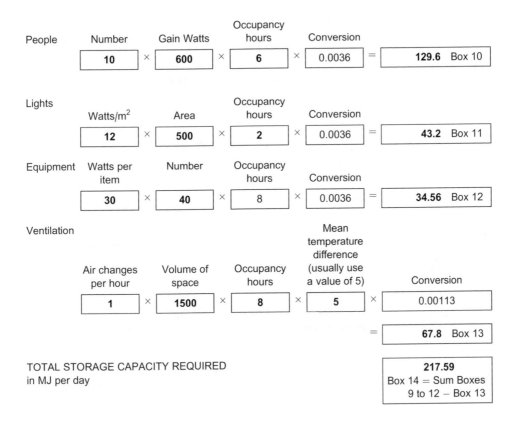

People   Number   Gain Watts   Occupancy hours   Conversion

| 10 | × | 600 | × | 6 | × | 0.0036 | = | 129.6 Box 10 |

Lights   Watts/m²   Area   Occupancy hours   Conversion

| 12 | × | 500 | × | 2 | × | 0.0036 | = | 43.2 Box 11 |

Equipment   Watts per item   Number   Occupancy hours   Conversion

| 30 | × | 40 | × | 8 | × | 0.0036 | = | 34.56 Box 12 |

Ventilation   Air changes per hour   Volume of space   Occupancy hours   Mean temperature difference (usually use a value of 5)   Conversion

| 1 | × | 1500 | × | 8 | × | 5 | × | 0.00113 |

= 67.8 Box 13

TOTAL STORAGE CAPACITY REQUIRED
in MJ per day

217.59
Box 14 = Sum Boxes
9 to 12 − Box 13

Step 3. Establish areas available for storage

Area to be used for storage		% stored in element		Storage required kJ/m² K
Walls	**48** Box 15	m²	**0.088** Box 19 = Box 15/Box 18	**19.15** Box 22 = Box 14 × Box 19	**399** Box 22 × 1000/Box 15
Ceiling	**500** Box 16	m²	**0.912** Box 20 = Box 16/Box 18	**198.4** Box 23 = Box 14 × Box 20	**397** Box 23 × 1000/Box 16
Floor	Box 17	m²	Box 21 = Box 17/Box 18	Box 24 = Box 14 × Box 21	Box 24 × 1000/Box 17
Total	**548** Box 18 = Box 15 + Box 16 + Box 17				

From Step 3 it has been established that we require storage capacity of 399 kJ/m² K in the walls and 397 kJ/m² K in the ceiling.

Using the graphs it can be found that the following selections would meet the load requirements.

Brick walls   Density of 1500 kg/m³ with a thickness of 0.3 m

Concrete ceiling   Density of 2000 kg/m³ with a thickness of 0.22 m

It must be remembered that this calculation is for a temperature rise in the structure of 1°C and in reality it is possible for this rise to be between 2 and 5°C. The result is that in theory up to about five times the stated loads could be accommodated in this structure.

Design pointer

• Provided that there is a means of cooling the structure, investigate the use of thermal mass using the above procedure or that set out in Section 2.

Selecting the service system

To give some indication of the type of service system that would be appropriate in the building, the flow chart can be used to determine the type of system most appropriate to the design.

Provision of appropriate service space within the building

Before it is possible to determine how much space should be left for mechanical services plant and service voids, it is necessary to have an idea of the type of services which are likely to be used in the building. Table 3.9 illustrates for a range of services systems the requirements of the space in which they are to be positioned.

Table 3.9 Requirements of main items of equipment

Item	Requirements	Best position
Boilers	Require good access of maintenance. Can be noisy. Large boilers can be relatively heavy. Depending on fuel may need to be near supply – oil or wood burning boilers need to be near the storage areas. Need a source of air for combustion.	Usually easier to position in basement or ground floors. Gas boilers can be positioned anywhere in the building provided there is good ventilation (natural ventilation is best). Remember: where air gets in noise gets out. Require good access – do you fancy manoeuvring a burner weighing 30–50 kg down two flights of narrow stairs?
Refrigeration machines	Can be heavy and noisy. Require good access for maintenance.	Best positioned low down in the building. Spare parts can be cumbersome and heavy and therefore good access is necessary.
Cooling towers	Can be noisy. Require a good source of air to provide the cooling.	Best positioned high up in a building – usually on the roof but can be behind louvres.
Air handling units	Can be bulky but are relatively light. Noise need not be a problem – they can be soundproofed. Require good access for regular maintenance – changing filters is the most common servicing requirement.	Can be positioned anywhere in the building. Best positioned near an outside wall so that air is easily supplied and extracted.
Electrical sub-stations and distribution boards	Can be noisy. Need air for cooling. Risk of fire. Sub-stations can be heavy.	Best positioned near an outside wall so that fresh air can enter and access is easy. If possible locate remotely from the building.

Table 3.9 Continued

Item	Requirements	Best position
Lift motor room	Hydraulic lifts. Cable lifts.	Require a pit for ram. Motor room at top of lift.
Pumps	These are associated with liquid circulation.	Positioned near main equipment.
Water purification (swimming pools)	Need regular maintenance. Can be heavy.	At ground level and near to pool.
Thermal stores (water)	These are heavy, large and well insulated.	At ground level.
Fuel storage	Heavy, risk of fire and needs easy access for delivery.	Locate near boiler room at or below ground level.
Cold water storage	Usually located above all water distribution systems. Imposes a heavy load on structure. In tall buildings up to about 75% may be stored at ground level.	Depending on size of building either all storage at high level or in tall buildings about 25% at high level the rest at ground or below ground level.

Plant room space allocation

Even if the building form is not fixed it is possible to allocate an approximate amount of space for plant rooms. Table 3.10 indicates acceptable ranges of areas for a selection of building types and size.

Table 3.10 Suggested space for plant. In large buildings in each category use the smaller percentage

Building type	Range of plant room areas as percentage of gross floor area
Factory or warehouse	3–4
Heated buildings such as offices, hotels, hostels	4–5
Air conditioned offices	5–9
Museums, galleries, theatres, concert halls and other places of assembly	9–11
Shopping centres	5–8
Swimming pools and other large sporting facilities	5–12
Highly serviced buildings such as hospitals	9–15

In a mechanically ventilated building if it is decided to position all the heavy equipment at ground floor level and the air handling equipment on the roof, then it is likely that some 60% of the total plant room space will be on the roof.

All buildings require some space for services. Even though the design may be for a super-insulated structure with no heating requirements, there will still be the need for electricity wires, water pipes etc. The larger the building and the more complex it is, then the services will require more space both for the main plant but also for distribution. Ensuring that sufficient space is left for services can be a designer's nightmare as more often than not there will be some conflict between the design requirements and the services allocation. Also, it must be remembered that services will need to be maintained and pieces changed from time to time and therefore they must be easily accessible for these requirements. Figure 3.10 illustrates for a typical boiler house the access requirements for servicing the boiler. Similar space requirements are advisable for other pieces of equipment such as air handling units, chillers, condensers and fans. Also, remember that the services systems will have a life span significantly shorter than the building and they will have to be replaced. Consider how the equipment will be removed from the building and how new equipment will be fitted.

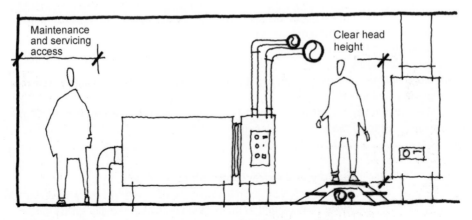

Figure 3.10 *Typical boiler room with the space requirements for servicing*

Location of space

There is no one way to service a building and the design of the services can be extremely flexible. Therefore it is not possible to say that particular pieces of plant must be positioned in a certain part of the building. For example, it is perfectly acceptable to position large refrigeration plant on a rooftop plant room of a 15 storey building but there may be consequences for easy access of servicing and structural implications – heavy plant on top of a building may need extra structural strength to take the larger loads.

The simplest way of tackling this problem is to look at the design and decide which plant is likely to be the most problematic and position this in an appropriate location. This can be done by referring back to Table 3.9.

Ideally a plant room should be either square or rectangular so that there is plenty of space to position plant in such a way so as to make servicing easier. Narrow plant rooms can result in the equipment being squeezed into inappropriate spaces and consequently difficult to maintain or replace. Access to plant rooms is another important aspect which can sometimes be overlooked at the early stages in the design process. Awkward access again detracts from the efficient servicing of equipment. Pumps are heavy pieces of equipment, and filter replacements, although light, may be bulky and therefore designs which make access easy are to be encouraged.

Design pointers – size and location of plant rooms

- Establish the type of system to be used in the building.
- Decide on the locations of the plant rooms.
- Estimate the likely area to be allocated.
- Ensure that the space is not long and thin, as this may give problems with servicing or replacing equipment.
- Think about access for servicing – carrying heavy pumps up a narrow stairway will not be appreciated by the service engineers.

Supply and extract from plant rooms

One common problem faced in the design of mechanical ventilation systems is related to the position of inlet and outlet grilles for the main plant rooms. Return air from a building is often partially recycled before the unwanted portion is discharged into the atmosphere. Particularly where heat wheels or static recuperators are used, the fresh air and waste air ducts are in close proximity. The natural thing to do is to vent both flows to the outside on the same

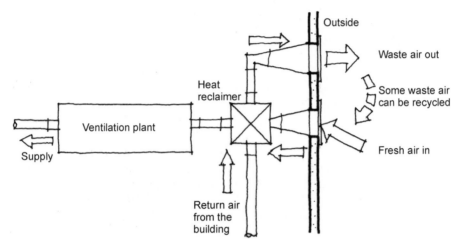

Figure 3.11 *Typical duct connections for heat reclaim indicate the proximity of the fresh and waste air streams*

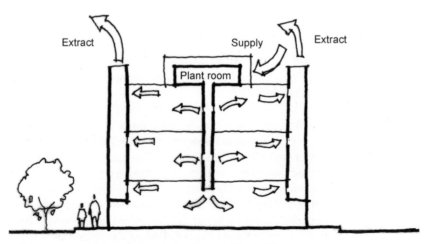

Figure 3.12 *Design of inlet and exhaust air systems in the building*

Figure 3.13
Modifications to the
original design to
ensure that fresh air
entered the building

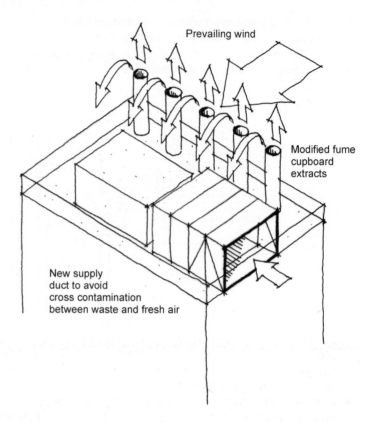

Prevailing wind

Modified fume
cupboard
extracts

New supply
duct to avoid
cross contamination
between waste and fresh air

façade. Figure 3.11 shows a typical example in diagrammatic form
and Figs 3.12 and 3.13 show a real example where modifications had
to be made.

Rooftop mounted condensing units

A common feature in the design of building today is the extensive use
of roof mounted condensing units. To ensure that these units perform
at their maximum efficiency, they require a good circulation of air to
pass over them. When installed in close proximity to each other there
will be the tendency for air which has passed through the first bank
(and been warmed) to partially be drawn into the second bank. This
has the effect of reducing the ability of the second bank to meet the
required cooling load. Figure 3.14 shows the effect.

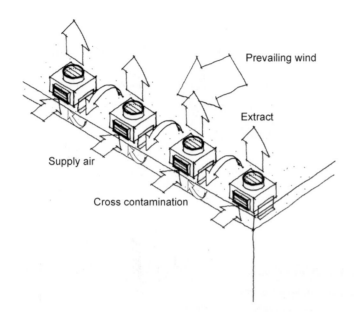

Figure 3.14
Effect of wind on the air flow patterns over condenser units

Prevailing wind

Extract

Supply air

Cross contamination

Design pointers – position of air inlets/outlets and condensing units

- Establish the prevailing wind directions and note any large building in the proximity which may cause local turbulence.
- Position air inlets to take advantage of the prevailing winds.
- Position the air exhausts on the opposite side to the prevailing winds.
- If not possible, design a rotating grillage system to ensure that the two air streams do not mix.
- Ensure that the spacing between condensing units is at least twice the width of the units.

Distribution from the plant rooms to point of use

Once the location of the plant rooms has been decided, it is necessary to consider the distribution system from the plant room to the point of entry to the space. Ductwork can be large and take up considerable horizontal and vertical space and therefore needs to be carefully considered. Large electrical cables are usually covered in a metal casing which does not bend easily and therefore getting such cables around corners can often result in a radius of over 1 m.

If these and other servicing issues are not thought about until the final drawing stages, there is the risk of extra work being necessary and the service systems not functioning as well as they could.

Efficiency of distribution

If the allocation of distribution voids/space is carried out efficiently, there are likely to be fewer issues with respect to excessive duct runs, pressure losses, inadequate space for servicing components etc. One definition of efficient distribution space is: 'Providing simple but adequate connections between the point of generation to point of use of energy systems'.

Design pointers – distribution space

- There should be logical connections between vertical or horizontal duct spaces and plant rooms. Avoid trying to fit services in restricted or narrow spaces. Try not to pass through fire barriers or thread services around awkward corners.
- It is better to position duct voids at the edge of plant rooms – this maximises the use of floor space in the plant room.
- Air is required for boilers and air handling units – make sure that this can be easily supplied without the need for mechanical means.
- Boilers need flues – make sure that the flue runs through each floor (in a vertical line: bends do not help).
- Straight lines are the shortest route between two points and the same applies to service runs. In air distribution systems, by keeping bends to a minimum you are reducing the pressure losses in the ductwork which helps to reduce the fan size needed. You are also minimising noise in the ducts caused by turbulence created at bends.

Sizing the ducts

One of the most important issues for the architect is to ensure that the spaces left for ductwork are adequate, as if not, changes will have to be made later on in the design (or even at installation) of the service systems. Having decided on the routes through the building which the service voids can take, the next stage is to estimate the size of these ducts. Ductwork can be large and take up what may appear to be significant space in a building and therefore it advisable to have an approximate idea of the sizes involved.

Buildings with mechanical ventilation will have both supply and extract systems and sometimes they will be running in parallel, which in effect doubles the size of the service zone. Take for example a six storey building with six air changes per hour with a total floor area of 1800 m^2. The supply duct will be in the order of 1.25 m square or 1.4 m diameter. Double this for supply and extract, add about 20 cm per duct for thermal insulation and a bit for fixing and a space about 4.5 m^2 will be required. This is not insignificant.

Estimating the size of the ducts
To obtain a rough estimate of the likely size of the ductwork for a building or part of a building need not be a difficult task early on in the design as it is possible to make several realistic assumptions about the design as set out below.

Step 1
From the performance specification determine the likely air change rate for the building (or zone).

Step 2
Calculate the volume of the building or zone to be serviced by the ductwork.

Step 3
From Fig. 3.15 determine the flow rate required (in m^3/s).

Step 4
Knowing the volume of air required, select the appropriate velocity in the duct. Most systems use velocities in the region of 6 m/s, but lower velocities may be appropriate in spaces where noise may be a problem – recording studios for example. Conversely, in large buildings it may be appropriate to use higher velocities for the main distribution (to cut down on the physical size of the duct). Having selected the most appropriate velocity use Figs 3.16, 3.17 or 3.18 to

Figure 3.15
*Establishing the air
volume and flow rate
needed in the building
or zone*

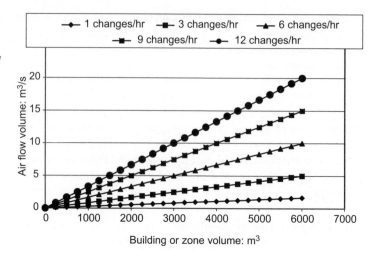

Building or zone volume: m³

Figure 3.16
*Duct dimensions for
low velocity systems.
Use where duct noise
could be a problem or
there is a wish to
reduce the fan power
to move the air*

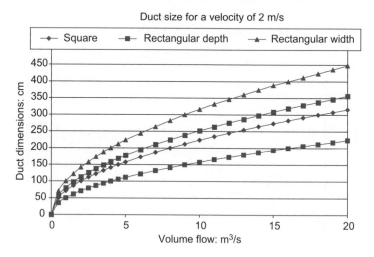

determine the duct size. Each graph gives the option of using either a circular, square or rectangular duct.

Step 5
Remember most mechanical ventilation systems will have both supply and extract ductwork and therefore these sizes should be doubled – one for supply and one for extract.

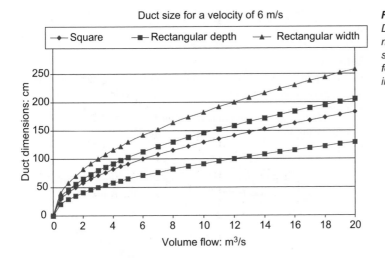

Figure 3.17
Duct dimensions for normal velocity systems. The situation found most frequently in buildings

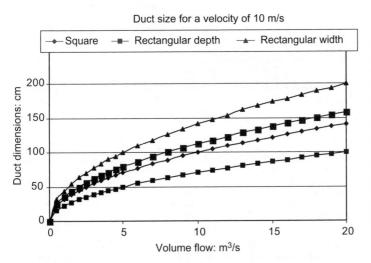

Figure 3.18
Duct dimensions for high velocity systems. In larger buildings where there is a desire to cut down on the size of the ducts – but remember at this velocity there is a danger that there could be noise breakout from the ducts and special measures have to be taken at the outlets to prevent noise entering the space

Example

An office building with a total floor area of $3000\,\text{m}^2$ is to have a mechanical ventilation system. The system will supply warmed and filtered air to the building and extract the waste air. Determine the size of the main distribution duct from the plant room. It has been established that six air changes per hour are appropriate for this situation.

Solution

This is a simple case. There is no requirement for either very low or very high velocities in the duct, so normal 6 m/s velocity is appropriate.

Step 1. Using Fig. 3.19 establish the air flow rate $= 5\,\text{m}^3/\text{s}$
Step 2. Using Fig. 3.20 (for a duct velocity of 6 m/s), the sizes are:

Figure 3.19
Air flow rates for a range of building or zone volumes and air change rates

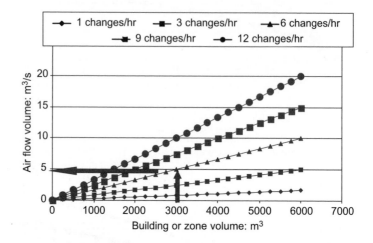

Figure 3.20
Duct size for a velocity of 6 m/s

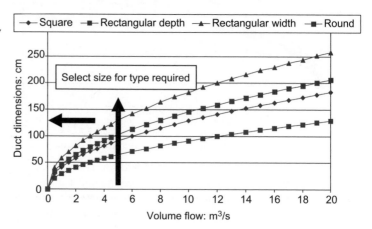

For a square duct = 0.9 m
For a circular duct = 1 m diameter
For a rectangular duct, width = 1.3 m, depth = 0.65 m

Remember to double the size to allow for both supply and extract. Also, you may wish to add thermal insulation, so allow at least another 0.4–0.5 m.

Assume you select a square duct, then the void area will need to be

Supply = 0.9 m + insulation of 0.4 giving a total of 1.3 m
Extract = 0.9 m + insulation of 0.4 giving a total of 1.3 m

So overall size is 1.3 m by 1.3 m.

If there are several zones within the building, an approximate estimation of the service void depth can be made by adding the zones together and carrying out the procedure outlined above.

Example

Figure 3.21 shows for a simple five-zone building how the ductwork would be provided to supply air to each zone. The ductwork will reduce in size as it moves from zone to zone. The way in which the size can be found is by carrying out the procedure set out above for each zone, remembering that the ductwork may be carrying air not only for that zone – the ductwork entering zone 3 will be able to supply air to zones 3, 5, 2 and 1. If each zone has a volume flow of X, the duct size will be given by working out the size in each zone as set out

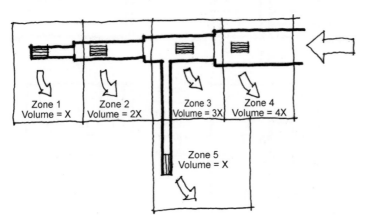

Figure 3.21
Illustration of how to estimate the size of ductwork for a multi-zone building

in the diagram. For each zone establish the volume of air to be supplied/extracted and by using the graphs determine the size of the duct. Each zone is in series so that air volumes are added together as you move from zone to zone.

Design pointers

- Estimate the size of the ductwork using the procedure set out.
- From the resulting sizes determine if the design can accommodate them efficiently.

If not

- Consider re-zoning the building.
- Consider relocating or splitting plant rooms.
- Look for alternative means of supplying the air.

Distribution to a zone

For air systems it is necessary to be able to distribute the air in ductwork or voids to the required zone. In most buildings the height of the floors will be set at around 3–4 m and the larger the ductwork the more difficulty will be encountered in accommodating it within the space.

Figure 3.22
Effect of the position of the entry point of a duct on the depth of the ceiling/floor void

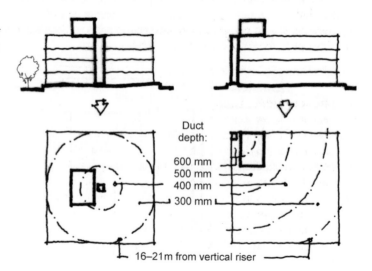

For example, take a zone with a floor area of 40 m by 40 m and 3 m high. If the space is serviced by a normal mechanical ventilation system, a duct with dimensions of about 2 m wide and 600 mm deep would be required. Anything much larger may be difficult to accommodate within the space.

By reducing the number of vertical risers the horizontal runs will become larger and hence care should be taken in ensuring that the horizontals do not become too deep as they may impinge on the provision of appropriate ceiling heights. For example, take the situation where there is an option to introduce the duct either in the centre of a zone or at the edge of the zone. Figure 3.22 illustrates the difference in ceiling or floor void dimensions in these two situations. By introducing the duct in the centre of the zone the void depth can be reduced by approximately 200 mm, which over say a 10-storey building would make an overall difference of 2 m.

Design pointers – distribution systems

- To keep void depths at a reasonable size (say 600 mm) an entry or exit point should be provided on a grid ranging in size from 15 to 20 m.
- Maintain a constant cross section on vertical ducts – you would not think of tapering a lift shaft.
- Services should not have to travel more than about 25 m from point of source.
- Place plant rooms no more than 10 storeys apart.

Distribution within a zone

For mechanically ventilated or air conditioned spaces it is possible to distribute the air from either high or low levels. There are advantages and disadvantages in both but to say there is one correct way would be misjudging a particular design. Perhaps one way of trying to establish which system would suit a particular building is to ask questions relating to the function of the building, the requirements for comfort or maintaining quality of product, and life expectancy of the building. Table 3.11 illustrates some typical distribution systems for a range of building types.

Table 3.11 Distribution systems for a range of building types

Function	Typical functions	Typical systems
Air conditioned offices	Flexibility of use is often the driver in these situations. Not only is equipment changed on a regular basis but also office layout is changed. Flexibility in distribution is therefore necessary.	Underfloor supply via raised voids. This allows for rapid change in office layout without disturbing the operation of the office. Good air circulation is obtained as the supply air enters at the occupied zone.
Mixed mode offices	These buildings tend to be designed for natural ventilation and the mechanical system used in warm periods to help 'flush' the building with outside air. Although changes in layout are possible, they will not normally result in major changes to the air supply system.	High level extract – usually along the corridor or centre of the building.
Schools	These buildings are normally naturally ventilated but there may be some locations where a mechanical ventilation system is required. Generally, such areas will be in operation for several years and flexibility is not a problem.	High level supply and extract. Where small children are concerned underfloor heating is often used as this avoids the need for radiators which can be dangerous if a child falls against them.
Sports centres	These are complex buildings. Where mechanical ventilation is necessary it must be designed to not interfere with particular functions. For example, high air velocities at about 6 m from a gymnasium floor may be satisfactory for football but not for badminton. Changing rooms will require extra ventilation to deal with showers.	High level mechanical ventilation in the changing rooms. Heating and high level extract ventilation in spaces such as squash courts. Underfloor heating in the main sports hall and possibly high level ventilation. In some cases it may be possible to use displacement ventilation.
Swimming pools	Specialist buildings requiring great care in design of the services systems. The high humidity of the air in the pool area can cause problems such as condensation and degradation of materials. Changing facilities also require special treatment. Cafés and shops which sometimes form part of such buildings have different requirements.	A variety of distribution systems could be used in the pool area ranging from high level supply and extract, to low level extract (as part of the water return system at the edge of the pool). Often the pool area is negatively pressurised to ensure that the moist air does not escape to other areas where it could cause problems.

Table 3.11 Continued

Function	Typical functions	Typical systems
Supermarkets	General comfort requirements coupled with storage of perishable products dictate the service requirements of these buildings.	High level mechanical ventilation, both supply and extract, with local chilled cabinets. Often these buildings do not include air conditioning as the spillage of cold air from the chilled cabinets is regarded as being sufficient to keep the building within reasonable temperature limits.
Shopping centres	These areas are devoted to selling products and display lighting plays an important part of service requirements. Often the deep spaces in these shops demands mechanical cooling.	The shops tend to be deep spaces and therefore demand mechanical ventilation. Usually this is achieved by having high level supply and extract systems. In some shops this is supplemented by direct expansion cooling systems which recycle air from the shop and cool it. Localised electric heating is sometimes used over entrances to prevent the ingress of cold outside air (this wasteful use of electricity should be discouraged and simply recycling the shop air via an air curtain would achieve much the same result).
Libraries	General library spaces usually only need heating but in some cases where deep plan forms are used mechanical cooling is used. Specialist areas may need to consider the preservation of documents and in this case a constant internal environment is called for.	Radiator heating is the norm but displacement ventilation could be used in internal areas where there are no opening windows. Larger libraries may make use of full mechanical ventilation with some cooling.
Cinemas	Internal spaces, high occupancy and comfort conditions must be maintained. Often mechanical cooling is used.	Mechanical ventilation with cooling is the norm. Usually achieved by high level ducting for both supply and extract.

Table 3.11 *Continued*

Function	Typical functions	Typical systems
Theatres	Similar to cinemas but there may be high lighting loads.	There is some debate as to the best way to service such spaces. Being internal they require mechanical ventilation – low velocity displacement ventilation would be best as the conditioned air enters the space within the occupancy zone but there may be space limitations and if the velocity is too high then draughts could be felt. High level supply is perhaps the easiest to deal with, although the conditioned air has often to pass through a large unoccupied volume before reaching the occupancy zone, thus picking up some heat and possibly moisture before reaching the occupants.
Hospitals	Perhaps the most complex of building types with a wide range of service requirements from very simple heating through to very clean environments in the operating theatres.	A book could be devoted to servicing hospitals, but in this case you should as far as possible zone the building into areas of similar function. Operating theatres will require high quality air conditioning and therefore for ease of servicing should be grouped together. Mechanical ventilation with heat recovery is often used in other areas of the building and generally this is done through high level distribution systems.

Design pointers – distribution systems

- From Table 3.12 select the most appropriate system and incorporate it within the design.
- Check the size of the duct space and redesign if necessary.

Section 4

How to deal with environmental
factors at the design stage

Environmental sustainability

As outlined previously, it may not always be possible to address all or the majority of environmental issues for a particular site or building design. There are many reasons for this. It may be because there are particular requirements set by the client, the site conditions or planning authorities. Other aspects may be discounted because of the costs of obtaining them or lack of availability. For these reasons and many more not mentioned it is necessary to give some priority to environmental issues and in the following sections a procedure is outlined which not only helps to ascertain whether or not the particular issue is important or not but also gives a presentation technique which may help to demonstrate how well sustainability issues have been incorporated in the design. Table 4.1 sets out the range of environmental issues of a general nature which are important in the design of a building and this table can be used as an aide-memoire when considering which issues are more important in a specific design project.

Generally environmental issues can be broken down into the following main topic areas:

◆ site issues
◆ water issues
◆ energy issues
◆ materials selection
◆ indoor environment issues
◆ reuse and recycling
◆ social and economic issues.

Each of these main themes can be further broken down into particular issues. In order to keep environmental issues to a manageable level each broad topic has been split into five subcomponents.

Table 4.1 *Aide-memoire charts for sustainability issues relative to the design of a building*
(For the building project indicate in the spaces provided the relative importance of the issues. It is then possible to concentrate on ensuring that the important and relevant issues are dealt with first.)
Site and Climate

	Aspect	How used	Important	Slightly important	Not important
Climate	Sunlight	(a) Shading of buildings or windows or other			
		(b) Penetration into building – requirements for sunlight			
		(c) Used for energy collection			
		(d) Other use			
	Daylight	(a) North light			
		(b) Light wells			
		(c) Requirement for light			
		(d) Other use			
	Wind	(a) Directional effects on high ground speeds caused by buildings			
		(b) Power generation			
		(c) Effects on air intakes or outlets			
		(d) Other.			
	Rain or snow	(a) Ground water levels, need for tanking or proofing basements			
		(b) Drifting snow, effect on roof design or loading			
		(c) Water runoff and drainage			
		(d) Other			
	Noise levels	(a) Noise from adjacent sites			
		(b) Noise from your site			
		(c) Noise from your projected building			
		(d) Other			
	Other climate aspects	(a) Specify			
		. . . .			

Internal Environment

	Aspect	How used	Important	Slightly important	Not important
Conditions inside the building	Comfort	(a) Thermal comfort limits 　　°C mean . . . . 　　°C range . . . . 　　RH % range			
		(b) Visual comfort 　　Lux level . . . . 　　Glare index . . . . 　　Quality			
		(c) Acoustic comfort 　　Level in room . . . . 　　Level from outside			
		(d) Other			
	Process or machinery requirements	(a) Thermal			
		(b) Moisture			
		(c) Other			

Mechanical Services

	Aspect	How used	Important	Slightly important	Not important
Servicing of building	Type of mechanical plant	(a) Heating by radiators			
		(b) Warm air heating			
		(c) Full air conditioning			
		(d) Partial air conditioning			
		(e) Mixed mode			
		(f) Other			
	Type of distribution system	(a) Water			
		(b) Air			
		(c) Other			
	Plant room location	(a) Basement			
		(b) Split			
		(c) Other			

Mechanical Services (continued)

	Aspect	How used	Important	Slightly important	Not important
Servicing of building	Distribution runs	(a) Vertical			
		(b) Horizontal			
		(c) Combined			
		(d) Other			
	Electrical services	(a) Distribution boards			
		(b) Sub-station in building or site			
		(c) Distribution under floors or above ceiling			
		(d) Other			
	Lighting services	(a) Functional			
		(b) Aesthetic			
		(c) Local			
		(d) Control of levels			
		(e) Other			
	Transport	(a) Lifts			
		(b) Escalators			
		(c) Other			
	Other services	Specify			

The site

These stretch from the macro to an individual site. On the macro scale, developments can lead to deforestation, destruction of wetlands, loss of biodiversity and the creation of urban sprawl. Building to low density imposes strain on other infrastructure such as fresh water distribution, sewer pipes, electricity and gas supplies, roads and so on. Low density also contributes to greater use of cars and buses, adding further to our problems of pollution. Many housing developments are now being constructed in areas where other amenities such as shops and schools are some distance away, thus contributing to the greater use of the car.

More specifically site conditions can be broken down into the following.

Respond to natural climate and energy flows

This aspect of design is closely related to issues of site planning and includes:

◆ *Wind*. Identify if the local wind climate can be advantageous with respect to providing natural ventilation or prevent areas on the site receiving high wind speeds.
◆ *Solar access*. Try to ensure that the site receives as much sunlight as possible.
◆ *Noise*. Consider the impact noise will have on the proposed buildings and design to minimise noise impact either by providing shelter belts or positioning 'quiet' areas of buildings away from noise sources. Try to ensure that any noise produced on site does not become a 'nuisance' to neighbours.
◆ *Pollution*. Air pollution should be considered. Try to position openings in building façades away from polluting sources. Determine if the building/s to be positioned on the site will pollute the surroundings and take steps to minimise this.

Maintain and enhance the natural environment

◆ Trees, lakes, ponds, rivers and wild life should as far as possible be protected from development and where possible steps should be taken to ensure that the natural environment on the site or adjacent sites is protected or enhanced. One good example of how this aspect has been taken into account is on the Newbury bypass, where the runoff water from the road is collected in lakes and reed beds to remove the heavy elements of combustion and oil before the water is returned to the environment. Wild life can be promoted by the use of bird boxes and feeders to attract them back to the site after development.

Minimise footprint

◆ Compact built forms not only mean that the infrastructure of the site (roads, drainage and power supply) can be minimised but also the external surface area of the buildings is reduced, thus helping to minimise energy gains and losses.

Maintain and enhance local amenities

◆ Where possible, developments should take into consideration the local amenities such as shops, schools, meeting places and so on and to ensure that they are considered as part of the overall design. New housing developments often do not take into consideration the provision of these important amenities, resulting in greater use of cars and the provision (sometimes) of extra buses or trains.

Impact of development on the neighbourhood

◆ A large development can have an adverse effect on the adjacent buildings in many ways, ranging from the creation of noise, pollution, extra traffic, busy pedestrian routes and so on. These issues should be addressed in the layout of the site so as to minimise their impact.

Water issues

Building construction and operation use a significant amount of water. Approximately 16% of water use annually is used to produce building materials, and in the construction and operation of buildings. Since about 1900 the world's use of water in urban areas has grown by around 19 times, and industrial use has grown by 25 times. In contrast, agricultural use has increased by only 5 times. The total of readily available fresh water in the world is about 0.003% of the total water and as further developments take place fresh water is rapidly becoming the scarce resource for the 21st century. It is therefore necessary to consider carefully the use and provision of water on site.

Preserve watersheds, ground water

◆ Where possible ensure that the development does not impinge on existing watersheds and that ground water levels are protected.

Reuse/store rain water

◆ To prevent overloading of drainage systems ensure that storm water is held on site by providing control ponds, pools, storage facilities and wetlands.
◆ Keep hard surface finishes to a minimum so as to allow water to soak into the soil. Design drainage to keep water away from buildings.
◆ Design pavements to facilitate water infiltration into the soil.
◆ Retain or maximise vegetated areas on site.

Reduce consumption

There are several aspects related to reducing consumption.

◆ Use planting which is drought resistant to help in minimising the need for irrigation.
◆ Store rain water and use in the building as grey water for flushing toilets etc.
◆ Minimise the use of plaster and other wet trades.
◆ Use automatic control systems to minimise the use of water for flushing toilets.
◆ Use low flush toilets.
◆ Use automatic shut off taps.
◆ If possible specify white goods that have a high energy rating. This also means that in the case of dishwashers and washing machines that they will be low water users.

Maintain quality on site/buildings

This aspect relates mainly to the construction process where watersheds can become contaminated through the building process.

◆ Ensure that surface water is not allowed to enter the public drainage system before it is cleaned. This can be achieved by using settling ponds.
◆ Ensure that soil and other debris is removed from lorries and other vehicles before they leave the site.

Provide water features

◆ Water features not only enhance the amenity of a site but encourage wild life and in some circumstances will also provide local cooling.

Energy issues

Worldwide almost 40% of the energy used is for heating, cooling, lighting and ventilating buildings and in the UK it is almost half of the energy used. This emphasises the fact that buildings are important in the drive to reduce both national and global consumption of resources.

Reduce energy for heating. Optimise the building envelope

The design of the building envelope can have a significant effect on the overall energy performance of the building and care should be taken in the design of the façades. By careful design the demand for heating can be significantly reduced.

- Compact plan forms reduce fabric losses.
- Exceed Building Regulations requirements for U values.
- Optimise glazing ratios for heat gains, daylighting and artificial lighting.
- Investigate the use of shading systems, remembering that east–west orientations will require different treatment to south elevations.
- Use thermal mass to reduce fluctuations in internal air temperatures, which can also have an influence on the cooling requirements.
- Detail junctions between fabric components to prevent the ingress of unwanted air.

Reduce energy for cooling. Optimise the use of natural climate features

The demand for cooling can be reduced by careful consideration of the climate features of the site as well as by consideration of the internal loads. Using daylight reduces the dependence on artificial light which reduces electrical energy used. Natural winds can be used to ventilate buildings and provide a degree of 'free cooling'. If possible zone the internal spaces to:

- Maximise the opportunities to use solar energy.
- Maximise the view of the sky to allow daylight to enter the building.
- Maximise the potential use of natural wind forces for natural ventilation.
- Shelter the building from strong cold winds – this reduces the unwanted cold air infiltration.

◆ Shield windows from unwanted solar gain in hot periods of the year.
◆ Consider reducing the internal loads or zone areas of high loads together – this can help in minimising the spread of cooling services throughout the building.

Reduce energy for lighting. Integrate daylight with artificial light

The provision of good quality lighting not only enhances the ability of the occupants to carry out their tasks more efficiently but can also reduce the energy demand for electric lighting. Electricity is a high quality fuel and its production efficiency from fossil fuels is rarely more than 30–40%.

◆ Maximise the amount of daylight entering the building by providing windows with a view of the sky zenith – the sky is generally three times as bright at the zenith compared with the horizon.
◆ Where possible use clearstory, light pipes and roof glazing systems.
◆ Use light shelves to 'bounce' daylight deeper into the occupied space.
◆ Keep internal decorations of walls, floor and ceiling light to reflect as much light as possible.
◆ Plan artificial lighting switching systems to switch off lights progressively as they become farther away from the windows.
◆ Use electronic control systems to modulate the lighting switching and levels in response to available daylight levels.
◆ Select glazing systems with high transmission factors for daylight.

Reduce energy for equipment and processes

Boilers, chillers, fans, pumps and motors all use energy to provide the energy systems to keep the inside conditions within comfortable ranges. These systems can be designed to minimise the energy used.

◆ Use equipment with high efficiency ratings.
◆ The efficiency of boilers and chillers depends on the load imposed on them – the higher the load the better the efficiency. To maximise the efficiency of the whole system use modular units as

they will work at full load for longer periods and therefore the system efficiency will be greater.

◆ Use heat recovery, energy storage and desiccant dehumidification to reduce heating and cooling energy usage.
◆ Use variable volume air systems to respond to the demands of the users – low occupancy will need less air than full occupancy. However, care should be taken to prevent air stagnation and moisture build up.
◆ Use variable flow pumps and variable speed drives.
◆ Use zero CFC-based refrigerants.
◆ Use white goods with high energy efficiency rating.

Investigate the use of renewable and integrated energy sources

One way to reduce the demand on fossil fuels is to use renewable or integrated energy sources which in theory will not run out – unlike fossil fuels.

◆ Look at the use of PVs to produce either electricity to be fed into the building or used as direct current to charge batteries, for cars, computers, emergency lights etc.
◆ Investigate the use of the heat generated by PVs to supplement space heating systems in mid seasons.
◆ Consider the use of wind generators.
◆ Consider the use of heat pumps – generally for every kW of energy fed into a heat pump 3 kW of energy are produced. If the two units are free, i.e. from ground water, river water air or other source, then high efficiencies are obtained.
◆ Consider co-generation of heat and electricity.
◆ Consider the use of wood burning stoves supplied from harvested cuttings from forests.

Materials

This is perhaps one of the most important aspects when considering environmentally friendly design. Globally, approximately 40% of the total flow of materials is attributed to construction – roughly 3 billion tonnes per year. The manufacture of building products is energy and water intensive and contributes to pollution and environmental degradation. Some estimates predict that by 2050 there will be no tropical rain forests if the present rate of felling continues. The manufacture of some building products produces toxic wastes and other pollutants. Without a very detailed understanding of the manufacturing process, it is difficult to be precise about which products to use and which to avoid.

Reuse existing materials. Minimise waste during construction

The first place to start with the use of materials is to ensure that the site operation practices are such that waste is minimised during the construction process. This issue can be tackled through good site management and the selection of materials which do not encourage wastage. For refurbishment/rebuild projects the same issues apply.

◆ Specify materials which contain recycled products.
◆ Do not overestimate quantities – this leads to waste.
◆ Organise site storage – a tidy site results in less waste due to damage or loss of product.
◆ Ensure that delivery of materials to site does not result in storage being required for long periods of time – this can lead to damage of the materials.
◆ Use off-cuts for other operations on site.

Minimise use of new

Some building products are capable of being reused either in their original function or in another at the end of their life within the building.

◆ Minimise the use of new products – examples could be using crushed concrete to form hardcore bases for car parks instead of quarried stone, or consider compact designs which require less material for a given floor area.
◆ Extend the life of existing products – establish if there are sources of recycled materials available locally, such as bricks, flooring.
◆ Embodied impacts have already been used – by using existing materials it can be argued that the embodied impacts have already been used as the product had a life before you extend it.
◆ Design for disassembly – steel beams can be joined in such a way as to make disassembly easy.
◆ Where possible, use screws instead of glues.

◆ Bolt instead of weld.
◆ Investigate the use of prefabricated components.
◆ Use durable materials.

Look at embodied impact

Some materials use a great deal of energy during manufacture (aluminium for example) or have to be transported long distances. Both these aspects contribute to the embodied impact on the building.

◆ From published data establish priorities for the degree of embodied impact which is acceptable – in some cases the embodied impact can be as much as one third of the total energy used over a 60-year period.
◆ Establish at what point in the manufacture, use or disposal of the product the most damaging impacts occur and look for alternatives with less impact.
◆ Avoid products which have a high impact on the environment during production or end of life removal.
◆ Source products locally.

Look at reuse possibilities

Not only is it important to consider the reuse of existing materials but the potential use of a material at the end of the design life of the building is an important aspect to be considered for the future. It is unpredictable what the sourcing of products will be in say 25 or 50 years' time and therefore it should form part of the design to consider how the materials could be reused in the future.

◆ Select materials which will not degrade with time.
◆ For materials or finishes which could be reused ensure that they can be easily removed in the future – this aspect relates to the way they are fixed.
◆ Try to ensure that at reuse the material is not downgraded.

Look at life-cycle impact

Materials with a high level of energy input in the manufacturing process will have a more significant effect on the life cycle compared with those which are low in production energy.

◆ With high energy products try to ensure that they can be recovered at the end of the useful life of the building and reused.
◆ Set targets for materials.
◆ Look to source products locally.

Indoor environment

A healthy, comfortable and productive environment is expected by occupants of buildings. There are several issues which therefore must be taken into consideration when designing for a good internal environment as already outlined elsewhere. In order to help to produce a good sustainable indoor environment care should be taken when dealing with the following issues.

Define flexible thermal comfort standards
◆ By allowing the occupants to have a flexible indoor environment the energy demand for mechanical conditioning systems is significantly reduced.
◆ Provide good quality clean air to the environment as this will help in ensuring that the occupants' exposure to pollutants is minimised.
◆ Investigate the site conditions so that the location of windows and air inlet grilles do not allow polluted air to enter the building.
◆ Ensure that excessive moisture is not present in the air as moisture will promote the growth of micro-organisms which may prove to be a health hazard.
◆ Detail the building to eliminate the possibility of water damage through moisture permeating materials.
◆ In wet areas such as shower rooms ensure that the materials selected do not encourage the growth of micro-organisms.

Ensure acoustic comfort
◆ Excessive noise in an internal environment distracts from the feeling of well-being. If the noise is from the outside there will be a tendency to close windows and doors, thus reducing the possibility of using the natural ventilation.
◆ Ensure that the design of the mechanical service systems does not produce excessive noise or vibration.

Ensure that the lighting (both natural and artificial) does not produce glare

◆ Ensure that the correct level of lighting is provided for the tasks.
◆ Maximise the use of daylight.
◆ Ensure that the colour rendering properties of the light sources are appropriate for the tasks.
◆ Ensure that discomfort glare is eliminated as this will not only reduce the visual quality of the space but also reduce efficiency.
◆ Provide appropriate lighting controls to minimise the use of energy.

Minimise indoor pollution

◆ Use finishes which can be easily cleaned.
◆ Design out awkward areas where cleaning is difficult.
◆ Use finishes which do not give off chemical particles or fine fibres.
◆ Prevent air stagnation.
◆ Ensure that there are no cold damp corners which can promote the growth of fungi.
◆ Provide adequate fresh air.

Provide a pleasant ambience

◆ Ensure good quality daylighting or high quality artificial lighting.
◆ Provide an aesthetically pleasing interior and exterior design.
◆ Use quality finishes and furnishings.
◆ Use planting and art to enhance the interior and exterior quality.

Operation of the building and reuse of both materials and products of occupancy

The designers should not 'walk away' from the project once the occupiers have taken possession of the building and expect that the building will be run in an efficient way. There is a responsibility to ensure that the design is such that there are appropriate measures in place to help the occupiers be sustainable in their day-to-day management of the building. By paying attention to the following issues at the design stage, it may help the occupiers to do the following.

Define appropriate management systems

Quite often the occupier does not receive adequate information on how to operate the building. Fitted drawings are incomprehensible to the majority of occupiers and steps should be taken to inform them in a way which is appropriate to their understanding.

◆ Ensure that the best available and most appropriate building energy management systems are in place and user guides are supplied.
◆ Try to ensure that the staff responsible for managing the building have appropriate training on using the systems.
◆ Try to ensure that these guides are written in such a way as to be easily understandable by lay people.
◆ Allow a full year for commissioning of the building. With advanced natural ventilated buildings the operating principles need to experience all four seasons in order to check for errors in the system.

Minimise usage within buildings

To a large extent this aspect is out of the control of the designer, but by impressing on the client that part of sustainability is to minimise the use of products then it may be possible to influence the eventual management structure of the building.

◆ At all stages in the design process re-state to the client how sustainable the design can be and stress the role of operational efficiency.
◆ Use signage to impress on the user the need to work in a sustainable way.

Provide collection points for reusable materials

◆ Design these locations into the internal layout plans and also ensure that there are appropriate central collection points for recyclable materials and not rely on a 'skip' located at the back of the building in an inappropriate location.
◆ Make sure that the collection bins or bags are not too large. When full they will be heavy, which will make them more difficult to move and therefore less likely that they will be used.

Minimise waste during construction

This aspect is specifically aimed at the fitting out of the building and to a large extent has already been covered. However, by ensuring that the fit out is carried out in an efficient way then the waste in products can be controlled.

- ◆ Ensure that the sub-contractors do not over order wall tiles, carpet, paint etc.
- ◆ Ensure that the client fully understands the room data sheets and discuss them with him/her.

Minimise waste during refurbishment

This aspect is the same as the construction phase but as the building will have some fittings there may be the possibility of persuading the client to reuse some or all of the fittings.

- ◆ Establish from the client the specification for the refurbishment and discuss it with him/her to see if the 'new' element can be reduced.
- ◆ Look at refurbishment of fixtures and fittings before specifying new.
- ◆ If this is not possible ensure that the old fittings and furniture are recycled to other uses and not sent to landfill.

Social and economic issues

Improve local environment

- ◆ Produce a design which is aesthetically pleasing and the local residents and users are happy with it.
- ◆ Consult with residents to ensure that they are aware of the design and explain the concept to them – information almost always helps to reduce complaints.
- ◆ Pay attention to the surroundings and try to improve the public aspects of the development (if possible) by better paving, art, trees, quality street furniture etc.

Sustain and improve work opportunities
Provide local focal point
Install pride in local environment

- ◆ Through public consultation ensure that the users and locals have a say in the project and that their concerns and wishes are listened to.
- ◆ Explain the reasonings for the design and if their concerns are not taken on board explain why.

◆ Provide street furniture and/or landscaping which encourages users to keep it tidy and clean.

Use the building and site as an environmental flagship

This aspect is perhaps the most difficult as in most cases it will be the wish of the client that they have a 'flagship' building. However, through providing information on the sustainable issues incorporated in the design, it may be possible to state that the building is a 'flagship' building – at least in the context of the surrounding buildings. The BT Coventry case study could be said to be a normal commercial piece of architecture but the building has obtained an Excellent BREEAM certification rating, so in terms of the other buildings in the vicinity it is a 'flagship' building.

◆ Keep client and users (if possible) informed on the environmental aspects of the design.
◆ Stress how these aspects improve the environmental credentials of not only the building but also the locality.

There is a great deal of information to be gathered in order to establish the environmental credentials of a building and at the initial design stages it will seem to be a daunting task. To help in controlling the amount of work necessary a self assessment spider diagram approach can be adopted. See the end of this chapter for examples. The intention is to allow the designer to set priorities for the design elements which can realistically be taken on board and recorded in such a way that progress can be monitored.

This not only allows the designer to deal with the relevant issues but also provides the client with a degree of understanding of the issues and why some are more important than others.

Assessing environmental sustainability.
A self assessment spider diagram approach to sustainable design

Given the range of issues which could be addressed at the concept and early design stages of a building, dealing with sustainability is often seen as being too difficult a task. To simplify this task the use of spider diagrams offers a way forward and Table 4.2 shows the assessment record sheets.

Table 4.2 *Self assessment record of environmental engagement*
For each Issue there is a range of questions to be addressed and your answers given in the following form

Level of engagement with environmental issues	
I am going to give this item very high priority	**Score 1**
I am going to give this item quite high priority	**Score 2**
I am going to look at this item but not too closely	**Score 3**
I may look at this item if time allows	**Score 4**
I am not going to address this item	**Score 5**

STAGE 1 – CONCEPT

The Issues: 1 – SITE	Initial Score	Achieved Score
1. Respond to the natural climate and energy flows		
2. Maintain and enhance the natural environment		
3. Minimise footprint		
4. Maintain or enhance outstanding features		
5. Impact of the development on the neighbourhood noise/visual etc		

The Issues: 2 – WATER	Initial Score	Achieved Score
1. Preserve watersheds, groundwater		
2. Reuse/store rain water		
3. Reduce consumption		
4. Maintain quality on site/buildings or minimise local contamination		
5. Provide water features		

The Issues: 3 – ENERGY USAGE	Initial Score	Achieved Score
1. Reduce energy consumption for heating		
2. Reduce or eliminate air conditioning		
3. Reduce energy for lighting		
4. Reduce energy for equipment/process		
5. Use renewable energy sources		

Table 4.2 Continued

The Issues: 4 – MATERIALS		Initial Score	Achieved Score
1. Reuse existing			
2. Minimise use of new			
3. Look at embodied impact			
4. Look at reuse possibilities			
5. Look at life-cycle impact			

The Issues: 5 – INDOOR ENVIRONMENT		Initial Score	Achieved Score
1. Thermal comfort			
2. Acoustic comfort			
3. Lighting comfort			
4. Pollution free			
5. Good ambience			

The Issues: 6 – OPERATIONAL/REUSE/RECYCLE		Initial Score	Achieved Score
1. Management systems			
2. Minimise usage within building			
3. Provide collection for reusable materials			
4. Minimise waste during construction			
5. Minimise waste during refurbishment/rebuild			

The Issues: 7 – SOCIAL/ ECONOMIC		Initial Score	Achieved Score
1. Improve local environment			
2. Sustain/improve work opportunities			
3. Provide local focal point – landmark building			
4. Install pride/awareness of local environment			
5. Use building/site as environmental flagship			

It will probably not be possible to consider every aspect and therefore a decision as to the most relevant aspects that can be incorporated into the scheme should be made and acted on. In order to determine how successful the analyses of environmental issues have been during the design process, it is advisable to complete the diagrams before starting on the design. This is in effect a record of the aspirations of the project. At the end of the initial design phase the diagrams should be completed again but this time it will be apparent whether or not the initial aspirations have been met. In this way it is possible to keep a record of progress throughout the whole design and construction period. Figure 4.1 shows a completed spider diagram indicating how the project achieved more than was initially planned.

This process can then be carried forward to later stages in the design and the final analysis could be presented to the client when the building is handed over.

Blank spider diagrams for each of the environmental issues are given at the end of this chapter.

Figure 4.1
A completed spider diagram indicating aspiration and achievement

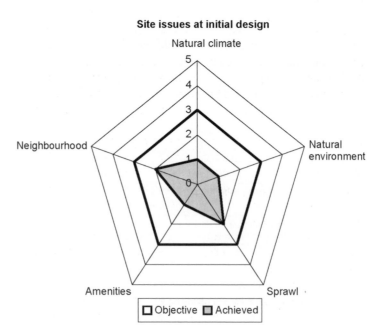

After the priorities for addressing environmental issues for a project have been set and an initial design for the building/s has been produced, it is necessary to test the design to monitor the effectiveness of the decisions taken. There are a few ways in which this can be carried out and although the descriptions of those which are easily available are intended to give an insight into how they operate, it is not the intention here to provide a full working method. To use these methods it is advisable to refer to the original documents or programs.

Levels of environmental intervention in the design process can vary depending on the ability of the site and design brief to respond to them. The issues relating to the positioning and massing of a building on a site are very relevant to the overall performance of the development in environmental terms. However, it is difficult to quantify this aspect other than by demonstrating that the design has, for example, better solar access than if the building was positioned elsewhere on the site – no real numerical benchmarks can be produced. As the design progresses and the building/s begin to take shape it is possible to consider in broad terms particular environmental issues. The easiest issues to start with are those related to the selection of materials. There are many ways in which the environmental aspects of materials have been defined and in the reference section there is a list of some of the sources. At this stage in the process the designer usually wishes to know if one construction is likely to be better than another but is still a little vague as to the basis on which the construction's environmental qualities are measured.

The desired answers to these issues are normally answers which state something like 'it would be better to use construction X instead of construction Y because it has a lower environmental impact'.

One way of obtaining rapid information on the environmental issues of constructions is to use the book *The Green Guide to Specification*. This publication explains the basis on which the environmental aspects of a wide range of constructions are based and then ranks the constructions in terms of a simple A–C rating where A is better than C.

Arriving at the A–C rating is a complex issue as 12 environmental impacts for the product are calculated over a lifespan of 60 years. For some constructions assumptions have to be made with respect to the number of times the material will be replaced over that period. The impact of the material, once calculated, can be in a range of units. For example the CO_2 emissions are in kg/m^2, while the transport energy is in kW. To equate the different units the BRE developed the ecopoint unit, which is the equivalent to the amount one UK citizen is responsible for in a year. One ecopoint is equivalent to:

◆ 320 kWh electricity
◆ 83 m^3 water – enough to fill 1000 baths
◆ 15 miles by articulated truck
◆ landfilling 1.3 tonnes of waste
◆ manufacturing 0.75 tonnes of brick (250 bricks)
◆ 540 tonne/km by sea freight
◆ 1.38 tonnes mineral extraction.

100 ecopoints = impact of 1 UK citizen for 1 year.
    The ecopoints associated with each element are calculated and the resulting range of values is equally split into thirds with the lowest third obtaining an A rating and the highest third a C.

Table 4.3 *Illustration of how the A–C rating system works*

	Nylon carpet, sponge foam underlay	80/20 wool/nylon carpet, recycled rubber underlay
Summary	C	A
Climate change	C	A
Fossil fuel depletion	C	B
Ozone depletion	A	A
Human toxicity to air and water	A	A
Waste disposal	C	B
Acid depletion	A	A
Ecotoxicity	C	A
Eutrophication	A	A
Summer smog	A	A
Mineral extraction	A	A
Cost £/m^2	13–19	31–48
Replacement interval	5	5
Recycled input	C	A
Recyclability	B	B
Recycled currently	C	C
Energy saved by recycling	B	C

Lookup tables are provided in the Guide and these present an overall rating as well as ratings within each factor. Table 4.3 shows part of the table for soft floor finishes.

From looking at the values given in the table the designer is very quickly able to arrive at a general summary of how products relate to each other as well as being able to see how a particular product performs in any of the individual elements making up the overall rating. This allows some scope for 'balancing' between different constraints.

One important aspect of the ecopoint system is that it also allows a comparison between the various construction elements so that where scope for diversity in design is limited those areas which are more important can be addressed first. Table 4.4 shows how the various elements break down in terms of ecopoints/m^2 of element, in terms of the overall ecopoint range for building elements.

Table 4.4 *Indication of ecopoints/m^2 for a range of structural elements*

	A rating	B rating	C rating
Floor finishes	<1.3	1.3–2.8	>2.8
Roofing	0.4–1.8	1.8–3	>3
External walls	0.5–1	1–1.9	>1.9
Doors	0.4–0.8	0.8–1.4	>1.4
Landscaping: boundary protection	<0.5	0.5–1.1	>1.1
Windows	0.5–0.95	0.95–1.5	>1.5
Internal walls partitions	0.3–0.6	0.6–1.2	>1.2
Landscaping: hard surfacing	0.4–0.8	0.8–1.2	>1.2
Upper floor constructions	1.2–1.6	1.6–1.9	>1.9
Sub-structural floor systems	0.4–0.6	0.6–0.95	>0.95
Ceiling finishes	<0.1	0.1–0.2	>0.2
Insulation (ZODP)	<0.1	0.1–0.2	>0.2
Insulation (inc. HCFCs)	<0.3	0.3–0.7	>0.7
Internal paints	<0.2	<0.2	<0.2

Design pointers – sustainability at initial design stage

- Look to the positioning and massing of the building on site.
- Consider the ecopoint rating of the main constructional elements.
- Select those constructions which are A rated.

As the design progresses from the initial concept stage and the design begins to firm up in terms of shape, massing and services, it will be possible to begin to consider other aspects of the design in sustainability terms. One of the ways of doing so is to ensure that, while the specification for the materials and services is being drawn up, that these specifications include reference to good practice and specification of low impact design (services) and products.

If access is available to the internet it may be possible to engage with the BRE Envest program, which is essentially a computerised version of the *Green Guide* but which also includes other aspects of design including building services. The results of carrying out an analysis using this system is again an ecopoint score.

An example of an Envest output is shown in Figs 4.2 and 4.3. These figures demonstrate that with this system a rapid estimation of the embodied and operational energy usage can be obtained as well as the ecopoints for the various structural and service issues.

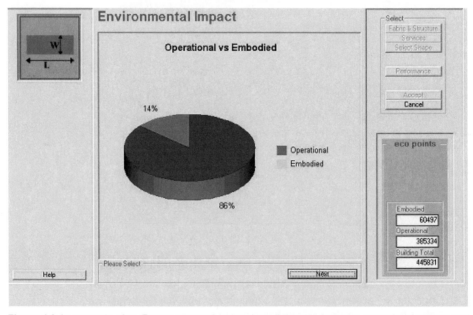

Figure 4.2 *An example of an Envest output showing the relationship between operational energy and embodied energy*

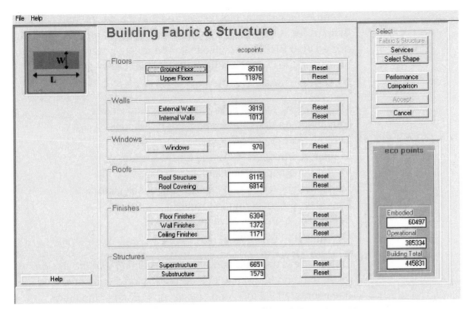

Figure 4.3 *An example of an Envest output for ecopoints of fabric and structure*

Design pointers – sustainability when shape and services are considered

Draw up a specification for materials and services which includes:

- Reference to low impact design
- Low impact products.

Finally, if the clients wish to have some formal record of the sustainability of the project, they should be encouraged to submit the design for the BREEAM formal assessment. This is an all-encompassing assessment of the environmental credentials of the project and will demand a significant effort by all members of the design team.

The BREEAM assessment

The BREEAM assessment procedures were developed to give owners of buildings confidence that their buildings had considered a range of environmental issues and that the design had acted on them. A fee is paid for having an assessment carried out by an accredited BREEAM consultant. The rating system is based on assessing the impact of the design on the following important issues:

Management: overall policy and procedural issues
Health and comfort: indoor and external issues
Energy: operational energy and CO_2
Transport: transport, CO_2 and location issues
Water: consumption and leakage issues
Materials: environmental implications of selection
Land use: greenfield and brownfield
Site ecology: ecological value of the site
Pollution: air and water pollution.

These core issues are addressed by ensuring that the design has taken them on board and has demonstrated this by providing documentary evidence and calculations. Each of the areas addressed are allocated a score and the total score is translated into a general rating of Pass, Good, Very Good or Excellent.

This is a two-stage process, the first being the submission of the documents and drawings to an authorised consultant who gives an initial assessment and makes recommendations as to how the design could be improved. After appropriate modifications the project is submitted for a final assessment.

The assessment is carried out at the design (or refurbishment) stage in the reprocess but no further follow up is included. It is therefore not possible to establish, say, after the snagging period, how effective the project actually is. Notwithstanding this, the system does ensure that the design issues are considered and acted upon (with evidence to show this) and therefore it is worth using this system.

Design pointer – sustainability when design is finalised

- Engage with the BREEAM team and submit the project for a rating

Summary

Designing for sustainability need not be an onerous task as many of the issues can be and to some extent already are included in the design process. There are several ways in which sustainability can be tackled, ranging from simply specifying products with known low toxicity (for example low toxicity paints) through developing site layouts to maximise the use of natural forces to a full accredited analysis.

For the majority of building projects perhaps the best approach is to consider the middle course, where design issues are considered along with specifying components and materials with known low impacts. The body of knowledge in this field is very fluid and is changing almost on a day-by-day basis and perhaps the 'middle path' is more appropriate. There will always be a need for the 'flagship' environmental design, which it is hoped will feed into the mainstream so that over time what was seen to be exemplar practice becomes good practice and finally everyday practice.

Spider diagrams for use during the design process

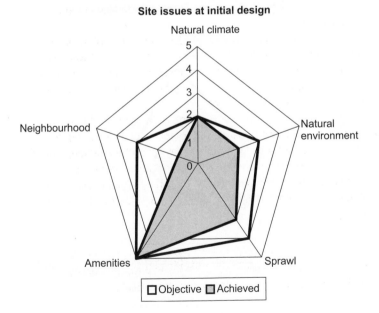

Site issues at initial design

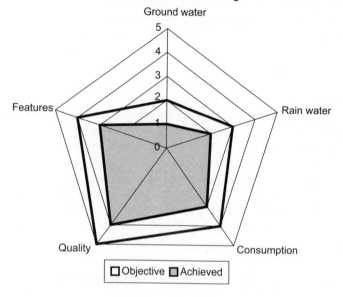

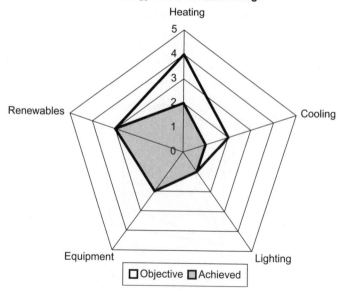

Materials issues at initial design

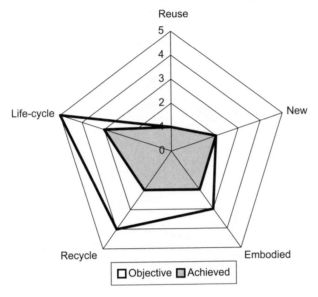

Indoor issues at initial design

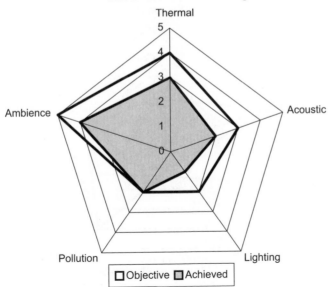

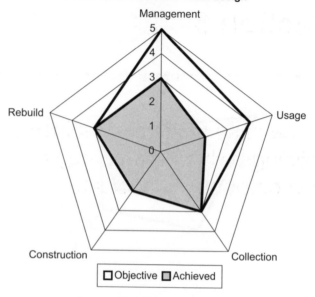

Reuse issues at initial design

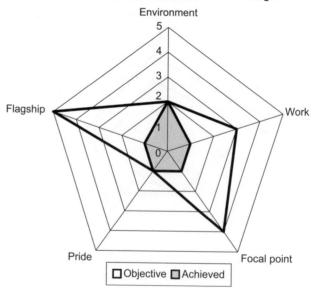

Social economic issues at initial design

Section 5

Some case studies of mainstream buildings which are energy or environmentally efficient

Case studies

There is sometimes the misconception that to produce an environmentally friendly or energy efficient building that the project must have a budget allocation significantly higher than would normally be expected. This is certainly true when looking at some of the more well known 'flagship' projects. The case studies set out in this section are intended to demonstrate that by applying the simple methods outlined in the text that it is possible to produce buildings which are either efficient in their use of energy or have taken on board environmental issues within restricted budgetary requirements. Each study shows a particular aspect which has been applied.

By looking at projects from the UK and Europe it is hoped that they will stimulate design to consider some of the aspects outlined. Some of the studies relate to buildings which set out at the design brief stage to be as energy efficient as possible while others had some requirements for energy efficiency but that was not the main design driver.

Perhaps one of the buildings which seem the least plausible in energy terms is the Dearne Valley College. The brief from the client was to produce a building to satisfy the educational aspirations for this part of South Yorkshire and there were limitations on the cash allocation. An energy efficient design was not one of the main design drivers from the client's perspective. However, the design team felt that by appropriate measures such as location, orientation and design for natural ventilation that they could go some way to producing a building which was, if not Best Practice, then very near to Best Practice. This was accomplished by:

- Looking at the optimum orientation for minimising solar gain.
- By carrying out an LT analysis of the glazing ratios arrived at the optimum glazing ratios.

- Investigating the percentage of the window which should be openable to allow for adequate natural ventilation.
- Limiting the plan depth to promote natural ventilation.
- Adopting a practice common in high-bay industrial units of bringing warm air from high level back down to lower level where it could provide comfort.
- Where the plan depth was felt to be on the boundaries for natural ventilation the application of passive stacks was incorporated into the design. These stacks also provide natural light to be delivered to the back of these spaces.

However, the ECO Centre project had a completely different approach to the design. The client wished to have an energy and environmentally friendly building and was prepared to spend above the normal yardsticks. The reasons given were that he could offset the extra capital expenditure against a lower running cost. Also, as part of the building would be placed on the rentable market, then he was able to offer a very competitive rate as the running costs would be significantly less.

A site investigation was carried out and it was found that there was a good supply of ground water at a constant 12°C. This prompted an investigation into the use of a ground source heat pump. The client was also very keen to try to be self-sufficient in energy and as the site was on old industrial land next to the River Tyne. With a back-drop of large cranes it seemed that a wind generator would not be out of character with the skyline. Furthermore, the client wished to use as much recycled components in the project as would be feasible. The design team then proposed the following:

- A building with a central atrium space which would be used as a circulation space and also for extracting air from the offices.
- The orientation chosen to minimise solar gains.
- An LT analysis carried out to optimise the glazing ratios.
- An underfloor heating system supplied by the ground source heat pump. It was also considered that in summer the water from the well could be pumped (via an exchanger) through the heating pipes, giving a source of free cooling if necessary.

One significant point to note about the energy systems in this building is the space required for the extract ventilating air. In architectural terms it could be regarded as being somewhat unsightly, having such a large prominent opening in the building. However, in design terms it is necessary to have such large openings and it is the responsibility of the designer to ensure that they are dealt with in a sympathetic way. On the south elevation of this tower are placed evacuated solar panels which provide the domestic hot water for the building. The wind tower has louvres on three façades which are opened in accordance with the prevailing winds so that there is always the ability to extract the air. Also, there are heat exchangers at high level to reclaim some of the heat from the extract air and also to provide some heat in winter to prevent unwanted cold downdraughts.

Sustainability aspects incorporated in this design include:

◆ The use of recycled bricks – care had to be taken to ensure compatibility with the metric dimensioning of the building and the imperial size of the bricks. Without recognising this there is the possibility of a mismatch in sizes which would inevitably lead to the use of 'specials', thus increasing costs.
◆ The use of recycled aluminium for the roof cladding – initially this proved a problem finding a supplier but eventually this was overcome and a UK manufacturer undertook to provide the extrusions required.
◆ The structural support for the atrium roof was made from old railway lines.
◆ The paint finishes were low toxicity water-based paints, which, despite having high environmental credentials, have proved to be less robust in use than was initially thought.
◆ Composting toilets were used in this project and they have proved successful, although there was an initial period when the occupiers (and visitors) had to be educated in their use.
◆ The carpet at the entrance to the building is made from recycled car tyres. This has proved to be a great success as there are a significant number of 'dirty boots' passing over it.

The southeast and southwest orientations required solar shading and to be effective it had to project vertically from the façades. The solution adopted was to use climbing plants to provide the necessary shade in summer while dying back in winter and allowing the sun to warm the spaces. The solution adopted was to construct a framework from scrap metal, and use redundant fishing nets as the mesh for the plants to grip on to. The mesh was held in place by surplus stainless steel cable from the shipping industry. To provide some interest in the shape the netting is pulled together to form an eggtimer shape by the use of recycled clutch plates from a vehicle scrap yard.

Recently a photovoltaic canopy has been constructed to supply electricity to power an electric car.

There are other less important environmental features incorporated into this design and in operation the building is proving to be very low energy, light and airy and is well received by the tenants. The Director of Groundwork has indicated that if he had had more funding available he would have increased the capacity of the wind generator from the design value of 80 kW to one at least twice as large. The wind generator has proved to be very reliable with very little maintenance.

Another office development with a completely different design approach was the development for British Telecommunications in Coventry. In this case the designers were given a very specific but tight budget to work within, along with a requirement to obtain the BRE environmental BREEAM certification at the highest level, 'Excellent'. Meeting the requirements of this certification focused the designers very early on in the process to investigate the fabric design in terms of solar shading, orientation, plan depth, window size and opening type with the overall aim of minimising gains and ensuring that adequate fresh air could be supplied through natural ventilation. Given the high occupancy rate of this building there was a need to provide a certain level of mechanical ventilation and some cooling. One of the ways in which the designers finalised on the fabric design was to look at examples from other recognised low energy buildings and to 'borrow' techniques from them. For example, the window system selected had already been developed for another building and proved to be effective, so in the words of the architect 'why should we always be re-inventing the wheel in our designs?' Care was taken to ensure that there was sufficient exposed thermal mass to absorb a significant proportion of the daily heat input from the operations taking place in the building. Recycled materials were used – crushed bricks, concrete from demolition of existing buildings on site used as hard core and low impact internal finishes specified.

The building did obtain the 'Excellent' rating under the BREEAM scheme and this project clearly demonstrates that within current commercial architecture it is still possible to meet fairly stringent environmental criteria without the need to exceed budget. A post occupancy survey carried out three years after occupation established that the occupants were satisfied with their working environment, although as would be expected there were the odd complaints of feeling either too warm or too cool at specific periods in the year.

Domestic architecture has produced many examples of low energy or zero energy designs, many of which are seen as being possible ways in which design should progress in the future. These exemplar buildings still form a small proportion of the housing market and one important aspect for the future is to establish ways in which such designs can become mainstream design. However, privately commissioned housing, although few in number, and usually given to small architectural practices, presents an opportunity for these practices to 'dip their toes' into low energy and sustainable design. For this reason the private house in Wirksworth was selected as a case study to demonstrate that a small practice can, through the application of simple methods, produce a building which is not only architecturally pleasing but is a low user of energy and is sustainable. The main aspects considered in this design were:

◆ insulation levels above current Building Regulation standards
◆ window area adjusted to minimise heat losses and maximise solar gain
◆ provision of stack ventilation to promote natural ventilation
◆ use of conservatory as a pre-heating device
◆ solar water heating
◆ low toxic and sustainable finishes
◆ use of locally sourced materials where possible.

The commercial study has been included to demonstrate that it is possible with this type of development to consider environmental issues. A site analysis was carried out and to a large extent the findings from this study informed the massing of the buildings on the site. Built into the brief were factors for shelter belt protection of more exposed areas and providing shelter to areas off the site which may be affected by this development. Individual building specifications were in line with best practice information and the use of natural features to provide a degree of site cooling was investigated.

The other UK projects featured in the case studies reflect many of the items already discussed but are intended to reinforce the idea that good energy and environmental design can be obtained within or very close to currently acceptable budgets provided that at the early stages in the design process the basic principles set out are considered and acted upon. It is clear from these studies that not all of the basic principles have been incorporated into every design, but nevertheless these designs still meet the initial aspirations of either the client or designer, which further demonstrates that it is not necessary to be able to satisfy every criterion to produce a good building.

The projects from Switzerland, Germany and France have been included to demonstrate how in mainland Europe the same criteria apply as in the UK. Again the case studies chosen were selected for their ability to penetrate into the mass market without being seen as 'flagship' projects requiring significantly higher resources.

The studies from Stäfa and Chur are the products of an architect who has been designing low energy buildings for over ten years and his overarching principle is that, by using simple but proven technologies, many of the energy issues just disappear. In all of his designs he pays careful attention to:

◆ orientation
◆ window size
◆ thermal insulation
◆ thermal mass
◆ ability to provide natural ventilation
◆ heat recovery
◆ control of solar shading.

These are simple concepts but as the studies demonstrate a very effective design is the product of applying these principles. This is particularly true of the Gasser project in Chur, which does not have a heating system but, to provide some degree of assurance for the occupants, a wood burning stove has been provided on each floor but in the $2\frac{1}{2}$ years of occupancy they have never been lit. One of the main drivers for this project has been the design of the thermal mass. The amount included is sufficient to store the predicted daily load from solar and occupancy and it is also interesting to note that even when the external blinds are not in operation that the internal venetian blinds direct the light (and solar energy) towards the ceiling. This has two benefits: firstly, to provide daylight farther into the space and secondly, to allow the solar component to be directly absorbed by the thermal mass without becoming a direct load on the building. The building energy management system controls:

◆ the position of the external blinds
◆ provision of natural ventilation through automatically opening the windows and also the doors at the top of the stairs leading to the roof (the stairs also form a natural ventilation shaft – compare this shaft with that on the ECO Centre in Jarrow)
◆ the heat recovery system from the building – fresh air is supplied to the building via a mechanically driven system and a heat wheel is incorporated to recover waste heat from the computer room (which is located in the centre of the building) and the toilets
◆ the lighting system.

The owner of this company is extremely satisfied with this building and has provided on their web pages the temperature profiles for the building since opening. To some extent this may be seen as a marketing ploy but it does demonstrate that the building does not overheat in summer or underheat in winter.

The Stäfa project is more conventional in that it does have a heating system, although very small, and the principle behind this project is very similar to the Gasser building in Chur. Appropriate thermal mass is provided, control of solar gains cross ventilation, heat recovery from internal spaces, and consideration of the fabric design for both heat gains and losses. The cost of this project was in line with normal domestic building costs in Switzerland.

The third Swiss project is the Uster complex. This project is the second of its type and the main driving force behind it was the 'balance' concepts set out by the Zürich city authorities. In essence these are that housing should be constricted which is environmentally sustainable, flexible, low energy user, provide a safe and secure environment for people and children and at the same time minimise the use of private transport.

The energy aspects have been addressed by ensuring that appropriate solar shading is provided, that orientation is considered and that the external fabric design incorporates an energy trapping system which increases the U value of the façade. The components of the façade are a translucent polypropylene plastic panel behind which is a honeycomb material, building paper, 500 mm insulation and finally plasterboard and plaster. The honeycomb material absorbs heat in winter (low altitude sun) which warms the outer layer, thus reducing the temperature difference between inside and out, resulting in lower heat losses.

Security and transport issues have been addressed by site layout and access to the buildings. It should also be noted that the site is close to both local buses and the railway network. Cars are parked away from the blocks, which help to provide plenty of usable space around the buildings.

Sustainability issues include choice of materials and preconstruction on site – which helped in reducing waste and unnecessary transport. Each floor forms a housing unit and the occupiers purchased a complete floor. They were then free to specify how they wished the floor to be divided. The central service core had provision for two kitchen units and two bathroom units, which gave flexibility in that a 'granny flat' situation could be easily accommodated.

The German and French studies demonstrate how environmental issues are being incorporated into school design. In the case of the Stuttgart kindergarten sustainability was the driving force, but it is interesting to note that the simple aspects of design for energy are also present, i.e. natural ventilation, use of high spaces to promote stack ventilation, appropriate glazing ratios and shading. Thermal mass has been considered.

The Calais project has been able to take sustainability issues farther and it has been included to demonstrate that with a little imagination on both the part of the client and the designer, exciting architectural forms can be obtained which are also sustainable.

Summary

The intention of these case studies has been to demonstrate that, through considering energy and environmental issues at the early stages in the design process, it is possible to produce buildings which are significantly better than normal commercial architecture without the need to be over-expensive or solely rely on new technology. This may seem to be an over-simplification of what is essentially a complex set of interactions between environmental and design issues. However, by making a concerted effort to consider them at the early stages in the design process, frequently significant savings can be achieved.

This has been borne out in practice through the UK Government sponsored Energy Design Advice Scheme and now Action Energy – Design Advice, where the major savings obtained particularly in energy terms have been made at the early stages of the design process.

These schemes have advised on well over 7000 projects over a ten-year period – which provides a substantial database of effective interventions. In the vast majority of these projects which have taken advantage of these schemes the main considerations have been broadly in line with the items set out below:

◆ site layout
◆ orientation and solar shading
◆ natural ventilation
◆ façade design for solar shading and energy losses
◆ appropriate use of thermal mass
◆ choice of materials.

Perhaps the largest investment in producing such buildings is in the time spent at the initial stages in the design process discussing with the client the needs and investigating design alternatives.

Building type: Higher education, Barnsley

Client: Dearne Valley College
Architect: Birkett Cole & Lowe Architects
Main contractor: Mowlam Construction Ltd.
Service engineers: N. G. Bailey and Co. Ltd.
Energy strategy: Energy Design Advice Scheme, Northern Office
Simulation specialists: IES, Glasgow
Client requirements: Low energy usage within normal commercial
    cost yardsticks. Encouragement of natural ventilation with heat
    recovery

Design details

This building was designed to make use of natural
ventilation and passive use of solar energy. The
classrooms are on an east–west orientation which
minimises the possibility of overheating in the afternoon.

    Water features are used to provide some degree of
passive cooling in the summer, and as part of the
environmental strategy provide natural habitat which was
missing from this site.

The glass rotunda at the top of the junctions between the
access corridors and the classroom blocks is used to
reclaim heat from high level and distribute it back to lower
levels.

External solar shading devices were specifically designed using IES software to determine the optimum size and location to prevent overheating in summer. The devices also act as a walkway for external maintenance of the first storey façade and windows.

Diagram of the IES simulation showing the sun patterns fall on the building in winter.

Dearne Valley College: Winter
9 Dec 11:30 Eye View

The ground floor classrooms on the north side of the building are provided with passive stack ventilation devices, which not only promote the use of natural ventilation but also provide some daylight at the back of the rooms.

The window openings are controlled by a building energy management system which determines when windows should be opened. The system has a manual override facility.

U **values**
Ground floor slab: 0.45 W/m^2 K
Walls: 0.45 W/m^2 K
Roof: 0.30 W/m^2 K
Glazing: 3.10 W/m^2 K

Energy consumption: kWh/m^2/yr

Design drivers

- Specific attention paid to natural ventilation provision both for single-storey and two-storey classrooms.
- Optimum glazing ratios and shading device design to minimise overheating and energy usage.
- Simple heat recovery from high level corridor rotunda reduces energy demand.

Building type: Commercial offices, Jarrow

Client: ECO Centre, Groundwork, Jarrow, South Tyneside
Architect: Carole Townsend, Newcastle
Main contractor: Sir Robert McAlpine
Service engineers: Entec Ltd, Newcastle-upon-Tyne
Energy strategy: Energy Design Advice Scheme, Northern Office
Client requirements: Low impact environmentally sound building and
    low energy usage

Design details

The underlying principles behind this
building were to produce a building which
was energy efficient and environmentally
friendly, within normal cost yardsticks.
However, during the concept stage of the
design it was decided to explore the use of
a wind turbine coupled to a ground source
heat pump as the main provider of heating
energy. This had the effect of increasing
the overall costs of the project.

The plan form of the building is a triangular shape facing
south. There is a central atrium space which not only
helps in reducing the circulation space but also provides
a mechanism for natural ventilation. The space is also an
important social space used by the occupants of the
building. The glazing ratios were selected using the 'LT'
method, which optimises the ratio in terms of the energy
requirement for heating, lighting and where necessary
cooling. In this building the optimum ratio was 33% but
35% was used in practice.

Materials

External walls. The building is essentially a timber frame construction with rockwool thermal insulation and an outer skin of recycled bricks from a Victorian warehouse. During construction care had to be taken to ensure that openings for doors and windows were consistent with the imperial measurements of the bricks and the metric measurements of new components.

Roof. The roof is constructed of recycled aluminium.

Power

1. A carport covered with photovoltaic panels provides electricity for charging electric cars. This is a recent installation and its performance has not been evaluated.

2. An 80 kW wind generator is positioned between the building and the River Tyne. This part of the Tyne is heavily industrialised with large cranes from shipbuilding and therefore such a structure was in keeping with the local environment. The electricity produced is used to power a ground source heat pump and also to provide electricity to the building. Surplus generation is sold to the local electricity supplier. Since installation the generator has been able to cope with the requirements of the building and has exported a substantial amount of electricity. Maintenance costs are low and the mill has proved to be extremely reliable, only requiring shutting down to clean the blades which do get dirty because of the exposed industrial environment in which they are placed. This shut down has only occurred once in four years and lasted for one day.

Heating system

Heating is provided by an underfloor system which obtains heat from the ground source heat pump. The water for the heat pump is provided by an 80 m deep well under the building. The water temperature from this well is very constant at 12°C, although it is a little salty. The salinity of the water meant that the heat exchanger and associated pipe work had to be made of stainless steel.

External shading

In order to give some protection from east and west sun, vertical external shading was used. This was constructed of a combination of old fishing nets, stainless steel wire (from shipbuilding), recycled steel frame and old clutch plates from Ford Transit vans. From spring to autumn plants are grown up these trellises, which provide shading. In the winter the importance of shading is diminished, which coincides with the resting period of the plants.

Natural ventilation

The building was designed to be naturally ventilated via opening windows and cross flows encouraged by a ventilation stack in the atrium space. In order to provide sufficient air flows it is necessary for this ventilation stack to be large. Such stacks in buildings are always difficult to handle architecturally and many do to some extent detract from the external aesthetic of the building. The stack in this building slopes towards the south, which provides space for evacuated solar panels (which provide the domestic hot water). On the other façades there are grilles which can be opened depending on the need for ventilation and also on the wind direction.

The ventilation grilles above the doors, which connect into the atrium space, are necessarily large and may need special acoustic treatment if acoustic privacy is necessary.

Windows

These were made of pre-treated softwood finished in low toxicity paint finish. They incorporated trickle ventilation to aid natural ventilation. The glazing system was standard double glazing units with low-e glass.

Other environmental features

Composting toilets. The toilets in this building use standard composting toilets imported from Canada. There have been some initial operational difficulties, mostly associated with users not being familiar with the operation of such a system. The majority of issues related to amount of water used for flushing the toilet. Once the occupiers of the building were familiar with the system there have been no major problems.

Carpet. One consideration related to the type of use to which the building was put. Being constructed primarily for groundworkers who deal with landscaping, it was inevitable that staff would enter the building wearing muddy boots. A carpet which was robust enough to withstand such use was therefore necessary. The carpet selected was made from recycled car tyres and has proved very reliable in use.

Paints. Non-toxic water-based paints were specified for the internal finishes. These have not proved to be robust in a commercial environment as they were prone to scuffing and in a short time the paintwork looked old. The building has had to be repainted and this time (although a compromise) they have used commercial low toxicity paints from a major manufacturer.

Use of recycled washing machine doors provides an interesting feature to the reception desk at the entrance to the building. These can be back lit to provide added interest.

Grey water. Rain water and water used for washing purposes is collected, stored and reused for toilet flushing and irrigation.

Outside the building there is a glass sculpture created from flattened bottles. This sculpture not only indicates the position of the main entrance to the building but also it was funded by the EU under their programme to encourage local artists. This scheme was also used for the artist to etch the glass panels below the balustrades in the atrium.

U values
Ground floor slab: 0.4 W/m^{2}K
Walls: 0.30 W/m^{2}K
Roof: 0.25 W/m^{2}K
Glazing: 3.10 W/m^{2}K

Energy consumption: 85 kWh/m^2/yr

Cost: within normal yardsticks for a commercial building. However, the installation of the wind generator plus associated electrical works and the bore hole increased the services costs by approximately 20%.

Design drivers
- Specific attention paid to natural ventilation provision.
- Optimum glazing ratios plan form and shading devices design to minimise overheating and energy usage.
- Extensive use of recycled products.
- Use of renewable energy.

Building type: Commercial offices, Coventry

Building size: $7000 \, m^2$ ($75\,320 \, ft^2$)
Client: British Telecommunications plc
Architect: Corstorphine & Wright ■ Kenzie Lovell, Brook Hall,
    Brook Street, Warwick
Main contractor: HGB
Service engineers: More Lee and Partners, Birmingham
Energy strategy: Energy Design Advice Scheme, Northern Office
Simulation specialists: IES, Glasgow
Post occupancy analysis: Building Energy Analysis Unit,
    School of Architecture, University of Sheffield.
Client requirements: Low energy usage within normal commercial
    cost yardsticks. Also to obtain an 'Excellent' rating from BREEAM
    (Building Research Establishment Environmental Assessment
    Method).

Background

Many of Britain's largest companies are becoming increasingly aware
of the economic and commercial advantages of carefully considered
environmental design and its importance within the commercial
property market. In theory, companies that are recognised as being
sympathetic to environmental needs should find themselves more
attractive to potential clients and customers. This can be seen more
often than not in development document guidelines produced by
companies regarding the design of new properties.

    The majority of new office developments rely on air conditioning for
maintaining a comfortable and healthy internal environment for their
occupants. The use of air conditioning can be expensive both in terms
of running costs and possible harm to the environment and under the
current building regulations there is an onus on the designer to
ensure that the building is designed so that there is not an excessive
demand for air conditioning or mechanical ventilation. One company
which embraces the philosophy of ensuring that buildings, which they
occupy, are of a high environmental standard is British
Telecommunications plc.

    In the late 1990s, Corstorphine & Wright approached the then
EDAS-North office for advice on how to incorporate the client's
requirements into the design. The design recommendations
produced were as follows.

Optimised design recommendations

Optimised glazing ratios around 30–35%. The LT method was used to establish optimum balance between the need for artificial lighting and heating/cooling energy.

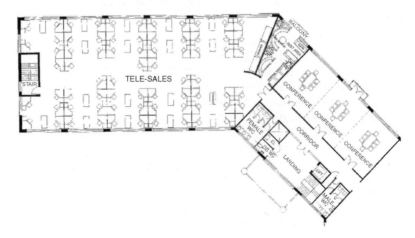

Typical Office Layout

Use of mid-pane blinds was shown to be beneficial in reducing the heat gains to the space and preventing discomfort glare but potentially could increase the internal peak temperature by 0.4°C as a consequence of higher use of artificial lights.

The floor plan demonstrates a mixture of open-plan and cellular office spaces.

Plan form kept to 14 m to maximise the ability to be naturally lit and naturally ventilated. This depth is also an economical depth with respect to the structural design.

Acceptance by the client of a more flexible approach to the internal specification of thermal comfort, in line with adaptive comfort levels. This has the effect of being able to design a building where the internal air temperature will be regarded as being comfortable when the inside reaches 27°C for short periods during warm weather. The main effect of this decision is to reduce the demand for mechanical cooling.

The heavyweight concrete structure including ceiling slab helped to absorb heat gains during the day and dissipate them at night – to space in cooler periods or ventilated out through night mechanical ventilation. This helped to reduce the peak internal air temperature by 2°C. This is due to an increase in thermal storage capacity, which reduces the rates of warming and cooling associated with a standard false ceiling.

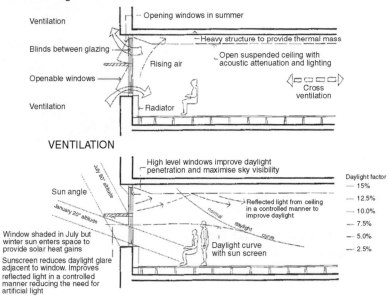

VENTILATION

LIGHTING

Building Section
Environmental Principles

Naturally ventilating the void above the ceiling slab overnight reduces the peak temperatures by 4°C. Ventilating this void at night cools the building structure. This allows for greater heat absorbency the following day as it adds to the cooling effect of the slab. The mechanical air distribution system is of the displacement type which allows for the distribution of air at low velocity near the comfort zone. This low air velocity coupled with large void ducts reduces the fan load.

Reduced lighting and equipment gains

Heat gains were reduced from an initial 55 W/m^2 to 30 W/m^2 by the use of energy efficient lighting and carefully considered computer heat gains. This reduced peak temperatures by as much as 4.5°C.

Environmental issues

In order to obtain a rating on the BREEAM assessment it is important to address many issues with respect not only to the design of the building itself but also to the impact this building will have on the global and local environments.

Global issues addressed

The site was a brownfield site that was previously occupied by one of the very early car manufacturing facilities in the UK.

The energy efficient design of the building ensured a low emission of carbon.

Recycled crushed concrete was used for foundations.

Local issues addressed

There were good connections to local public transport. It must be noted that as this building has 24-hour occupation, with staff changes taking place late in the evening when public transport may not be available, it was felt that car parking had to be provided for the security of these staff.

The building would not pose a wind hazard to other developments. There were no issues with respect to shading other buildings. The noise emitted from this building would not pose a problem to other developments.

Design and indoor issues

Mechanical and water services were designed in accordance with the BREEAM recommended Guides and Codes of Practice.

Where possible significant amounts of recycled timber and concrete were used in the construction.

Low toxicity paints were used. No insulation materials using CFCs in their manufacture were used.

Recycling facilities were specified.

The results

Taking on board the above issues, the architects were able to design a building within the specified commercial cost yardsticks ($£850/m^2$) and the building achieved an 'Excellent' rating from BREEAM.

Post occupancy analysis

A post occupancy study carried out by the Building Energy Analysis Unit, School of Architecture, University of Sheffield, concluded that overall the occupants were very satisfied with the conditions within the building, although some felt a little warm in the summer. This is to be expected when such a flexible approach is taken when specifying the internal environment. However, it is felt that on balance that this is a good building to work in. There was one issue, which was noted in relation to the acoustic environment. As some of the office spaces are large and there is a large expanse of hard ceiling finishes, office noise can be transmitted over the length of the space. This can be overcome by the selection of appropriate soft finishes to the furnishings.

U values
Walls: 0.45 W/m^{2}K
Floor: 0.45 W/m^{2}K
Ceiling: 0.30 W/m^{2}K
Windows: 3.0 W/m^{2}K

Cost: £850 m^2

Design drivers

- Use of cross ventilation coupled with thermal mass.
- Use of high quality window systems with mid-pane blinds.
- Use of recycled materials.

Building type: Private house, Wirksworth

Client: Private individual, Alison Richards
Architect: Derek Trowell Architects, 1 Greenhill, Wirksworth,
    Derbyshire.
Main contractor: Gordon Constable, Wirksworth
Energy strategy: Building Energy Analysis Unit, School of
    Architecture, University of Sheffield
Client requirements: Low environmental impact

Background

The client was very concerned about the environmental impact the
new house would have on a restricted site in the conservation area.
She particularly wished to use materials which were not damaging to
the environment and also to reduce the demand for heating to a
minimum. She and the architect approached the Building Energy
Analysis Unit to seek advice on the selection of appropriate materials
and how to develop the building so that it would have a low energy
requirement.

Design details

This is a three-storey residential house built on a steeply sloping
south elevation. This gave the opportunity to utilise a double-storey
conservatory space on the south façade. This provides passive
heating to the building through a ducted air system.

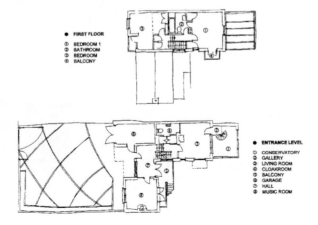

● FIRST FLOOR

① BEDROOM 1
② BATHROOM
③ BEDROOM
④ BALCONY

● ENTRANCE LEVEL

① CONSERVATORY
② GALLERY
③ LIVING ROOM
④ CLOAKROOM
⑤ BALCONY
⑥ GARAGE
⑦ HALL
⑧ MUSIC ROOM

GARDEN LEVEL
① GREY-WATER RECYCLE TANK
② CONSERVATORY
③ DINING ROOM
④ KITCHEN

The north-facing wall had the number of openings kept to a minimum to reduce heat losses and the wall was highly insulated to a U value of $0.2\,W/m^2\,{}^{\circ}C$.

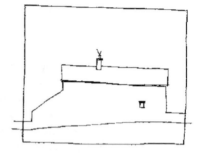

The south-facing wall is highly glazed to maximise solar gain. The windows are double glazed with low-e glazing and internal blinds to prevent overheating in warm periods.

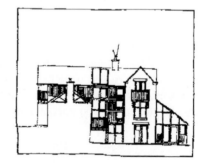

Roof mounted solar water heating panels provide 50–70% of the household's annual hot water requirement.

All rainwater is filtered and recycled through a tank housed underground. The water is then fed back into the house and used for non-potable uses.

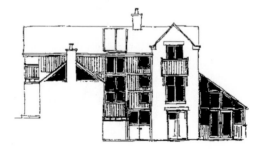

Extensive use of timber from managed local forests was incorporated into the design. The floor to the south-facing entrance lobby is tiled in ceramic tiles on top of thermal insulation, which adds to the thermal mass of this space.

U values

External walls: $0.20\,W/m^2K$
Ground floor: $0.30\,W/m^2K$
Roof: $0.20\,W/m^2K$
Glazing: $2.5\,W/m^2K$

Cost: £600 m^2

Design drivers

- Optimum use of thermal insulation, glazing ratios and weather stripping to minimise heat losses.
- Use of south-facing two-storey glazed entrance lobby for passive use of solar energy.
- Use of solar energy for heating and hot water.
- Use of locally sourced materials.

Building type: Concept industrial and distribution centre, Milton Keynes

Client: Concept scheme for Gazeley Properties
Architect: Corstorphine & Wright ■ Kenzie Lovell, Brook Hall,
    Brook Street, Warwick
Energy strategy: Energy Design Advice Scheme, Northern Office

Background

Many distribution centres are constructed near major transport routes and usually consist of large-span structures capable of storing a wide range of commodities. The main design features of such developments are often the ability to load and unload in a safe and efficient way. Environmental issues are not usually seen as being of high importance. However, with growing awareness of the environmental impact of developments, it is becoming more common to consider environmental factors.

Design details

This development proposed to use passive energy features which were aimed at reducing the re-running costs of the development and also at saving investment in infrastructure costs.

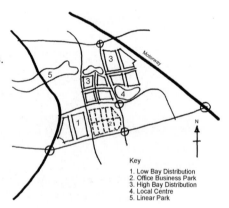

Key
1. Low Bay Distribution
2. Office Business Park
3. High Bay Distribution
4. Local Centre
5. Linear Park

Simple fabric measures

Typical designs for industrial units tend to produce buildings which have energy consumptions in the range 200–1400 kWh/m^2, which translates into costs in the range £4–27/m^2 gross floor area. Storage and distribution centres tend to be heated to a lower level than other industrial buildings and therefore the costs of energy for such buildings tend to be lower. The following simple measures should, as far as possible, be built into the designs:

1. Ensure that all joins between different elements are sealed to reduce the ingress of unwanted outside air.
2. Increase the U values of the fabric to beyond current building regulation standards.
3. Use (and specify cleaning periods) roof glazing to provide daylight. 10% of the roof is usually sufficient to provide daylight. Where possible care should be taken to ensure that the roof lights are over gangways and not over storage racks.
4. For openings use rapidly closing doors and covers over lorry access areas.
5. Orientate openings away from prevailing winds or provide shelter belts.

Site conditions

The site was bounded on all sides by other low rise developments. The prevailing wind was from the southwest and the south side of the site was open. The accommodation on site was to be a mixture of office buildings, low- and high-bay storage buildings. To maximise the potential for solar energy utilisation in the office development and to provide shelter to the more vulnerable high-bay buildings the low-bay distribution buildings were positioned on the southwest of the site. The office building was positioned to the south. The high-bay buildings were positioned to the north of the site.

Building services

Such developments tend to use simple heating and cooling systems, but there is the opportunity to be a little more adventurous as outlined:

1. Consider using local combined heat and power (CHP) plant to provide both heating and electricity to the whole complex.
2. In summer the heat produced by the CHP plant could be used to provide refrigeration (using absorption plant, which tends to be less damaging to the environment).
3. Provide a lake which could be used to dissipate waste heat from the cooling plant and at the same time provide a local focal point.
4. Where space allows, thermal storage systems could be used to minimise the peak demand for heat.

Design drivers

- Consider local climate and design to minimise high winds and to maximise solar penetration.
- Use of south-facing elevations for passive collection of solar energy.
- Use of solar energy for heating and hot water.
- Consider CHP plant and where possible link it to several buildings.
- Use of locally sourced materials.

Building type: Notley Green Primary School, Essex

Building size: 1040 m^2 (11 190 ft^2)
Client: Essex County Council
Architect: Allford Hall Monaghan Morris, London
Main contractor: Jackson Building, Ipswich
Structural engineers: atelier One
Energy strategy: atelier Ten
Client requirements: To develop a school building which respected
the environment and to build a Green School

Background

This school was designed to encompass environmental issues,
particularly solar technology and green issues. A requirement of
the design was to maximise the use of natural lighting and reduce
the heating demand, coupled with a desire to produce a good
piece of architecture.

Design details

The triangular shape of the
building coupled with the
creation of an internal atrium
space not only helped to
reduce the circulation space
by about 10% but also helped
in providing natural light and
natural ventilation. The compact
plan form helps to
reduce heat losses.

The southeast-facing
classrooms benefit from morning
solar gains, which help to
provide some heat in the spring
and autumn.

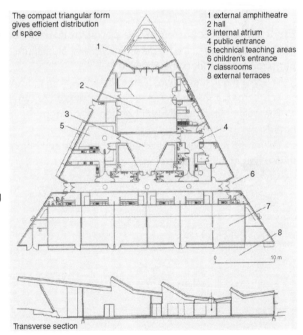

The compact triangular form
gives efficient distribution
of space

1 external amphitheatre
2 hall
3 internal atrium
4 public entrance
5 technical teaching areas
6 children's entrance
7 classrooms
8 external terraces

0   10 m

Transverse section

The glazing ratios are in the order of 35%, this being the optimum for preventing excessive heat losses and controlling heat gains. North light is allowed into the spaces by the clearstory lights created by the sloping roofs.

Having openings in the façades and overhead provides natural ventilation. In the central spaces fresh air is introduced under the floor (through clay pipes) and extracted through the clearstory windows.

The heating system is of the underfloor type which does not give rise to high temperature gradients in the occupied area and allows the temperature to be regulated by zone.

Environmental features in the construction materials

The window frames are made of timber and aluminium, which gives good thermal performance and low maintenance.

The Warmcell thermal insulation is made from old newspapers.

The carpet at the entrance is made from old car tyres.

The polyethylene wall coverings are made from recycled plastic bottles.

The green roof requires a shallow substrate and helps to absorb CO_2. It also has minimal maintenance.

U values
Walls: 0.21 W/m^{2}K
Linoleum floors: 0.37 W/m^{2}K
Wood floors: 0.38 W/m^{2}K
Roof: 0.32 W/m^{2}K
Glazing: 1.5 W/m^{2}K

Energy consumption: 142 kWh/m^2/year

Cost: £1150/m^2

Design drivers

- Compact plan form.
- Ability to use natural ventilation.
- Orientation selected to provide passive heating but minimise overheating.

Building type: Offices, Chur, Switzerland

Building size: 1400 m² (15 064 ft²)

Client: Gasser Baumaterialien

Architect: Architekturbüro Rüedi, Grison Park, Weisentalstrasse,
    Chur, Switzerland

Main contractor: Josias Gasser Baumaterialien AG, Chur

Energy strategy: Andrea Rüedi

Solar specialist: Ars Solaris, Ing. Raimund Hächler, Chur

Client requirements: Very low energy usage, low environmental
    impact and use of renewable energy

Background

The owner of this builders' merchant business was keen to ensure
that his new office block was as environmentally friendly as possible.
He included in the design brief a requirement that the building should
have no or very little heating requirements. The final solution relies on
the use of thermal mass, cross and stack ventilation and heat
recovery from the computer and toilets. As far as possible all
materials used in the construction are resourced locally and
extensive use of local timber is made for both external and internal
claddings.

Design details

This is a commercial office building which
makes use of renewable energy to
minimise the energy demands. It is
constructed of local materials and
embodies several environmentally friendly
products.

The south elevation is 100% glazed with a high performance glazing system. External blinds prevent the sun's rays penetrating the space in warm periods, while the plan depth of less than 14 m allows for cross ventilation.

The access to the roof gardens and photovoltaic panels also acts as a ventilation extract. Doors and windows on three façades can be opened (by the Building Energy Management System) to provide extract ventilation in warm weather.

The internal venetian blinds have a silvered finished with the curvature being designed to 'throw' the suns rays towards the ceiling where the heat is absorbed by the high thermal mass. They also act like light-shelves, thus improving the daylight factor deeper into the space.

The construction is such that 60–70 MJ/m^2 hr of energy can be absorbed by the timber and concrete structure.

The photovoltaic array is capable of producing between 70 000 and 75 000 kWh/yr of electricity. There are also solar water heaters which produce the domestic hot water.

A heat recovery system is used to provide fresh air supply to the building.

U values

External walls: $0.15\,\text{W/m}^2\text{K}$
(recycled newspapers are used as thermal insulation 240 mm thick)
Ground floor: $0.37\,\text{W/m}^2\text{K}$
1st and 2nd floor slabs: $0.14\,\text{W/m}^2\text{K}$
Roof: $0.20\,\text{W/m}^2\text{K}$
Glazing: $0.70\,\text{W/m}^2\text{K}$

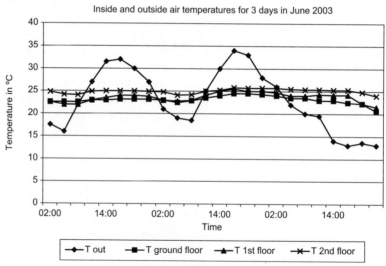

Inside and outside air temperatures for 3 days in June 2003

Even in summer when the outside air temperatures reach the mid 30s, the inside temperatures are still in the low 20s. In winter when the outside temperatures are well below 0°C the inside is still in the low 20s.

Costs. The building cost 3% more than a conventional building
of similar size.

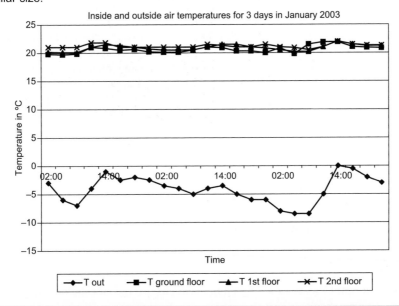

Inside and outside air temperatures for 3 days in January 2003

—♦—T out —■—T ground floor —▲—T 1st floor —✕—T 2nd floor

Design drivers

- Use of thermal mass in walls and ceilings to absorb heat.
- Maximum use of solar energy for heating, hot water and electricity production.
- Mixed mode ventilation controlled by Building Energy Management System.

Building type: Low energy and environmentally friendly housing in Stäfa, Switzerland

Client: Basler-Versicherungen

Architect: Andrea Rüedi, HTL Architects, Wiesentalstrasse 7, Chur, Switzerland

Main contractor: Batigroup Generalunternehmung, Binzmühlestrasse 11, 8050 Zürich

Service engineers: Placido Perez, Bonaduz Proplaning AG, Basel

Energy strategy: Andrea Rüedi, HTL Architects, Wiesentalstrasse 7, Chur, Switzerland

Background

This housing development to the southeast of Zürich in Stäfa, financed by Basler Insurance, was designed to be both low energy and low embodied energy. One of the other parameters set by the insurance company was that they should be within normal building costs.

Design details

The design concept was to create flats that make passive use of solar energy coupled with a mechanical ventilation system with heat recovery.

The blocks are highly insulated both on the external façades and also between flats.

One of the methods of maximising the solar gains was to place the balconies to the side of each flat rather than at the front.

The nearly 100% glazing is of a high quality and each element can be opened to promote natural ventilation when the climate is appropriate.

The north façade is well insulated with smaller openings to minimise losses.

The internal walls, floors and ceilings are constructed of dense materials. These give the building a considerable amount of thermal mass, which absorbs the heat gains during the day and releases them at night when cooler air removes the heat from the flats.

Building materials
External walls. Sandstone, rockwool thermal insulation, dense block work.
Roof. Timber, rockwool thermal insulation, steel profile sheeting.
Windows. Triple glazed 6 mm glass in timber frames.
Floors. Timber beams and timber planking to underside, concrete, screed and tile/timber finish.

Heating requirement: $3.1 \, kWh/m^2yr$
Warm water: $5.0 \, kWh/m^2yr$

U values
Glazing: 0.5 and $1.0 \, W/m^2K$
External walls: $0.16 \, W/m^2K$
Internal walls: $0.40 \, W/m^2K$
Roof: $0.15 \, W/m^2K$
Roof of cellar: $0.17 \, W/m^2K$
Area: $2422 \, m^2$
Number of flats: 22

Cost: $2970 \, SFr/m^2$
$£1390 /m^2$

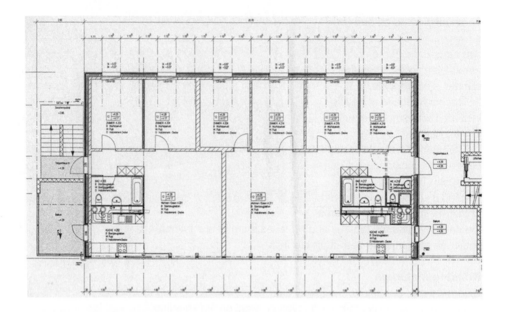

Design drivers

- Maximum use of environmentally friendly building products.
- Optimum use of glazing to maximise use of solar energy.
- Use of thermal mass to store internal heat gains for use later in the day.
- Use of locally sourced materials.

Building type: Housing balance project in Uster, Switzerland

Client: Developer, Andreas Steich
Architect: Haerle Hubacher
Main contractor: Steich, Zürich
Service engineers: Ganz, Zürich
Energy strategy: Highly insulated with air recovery systems to each
 floor

Background
The concept behind this scheme was to produce affordable,
spacious shared ownership housing of architectural merit. The
resulting homes meet these requirements and at the same time are
environmentally sound and low energy users. The blocks are
divided horizontally and the owners buy a complete floor which can
then be subdivided in many ways to create a wide range of internal
plan forms.

Design details
The site layout has the main orientation facing south on a
staggered plan form which not only allows deeper
penetration of sunlight (particularly in the winter months)
but creates interesting landscaped areas which are also
safe for children to play in. Cars are limited to the ribbon
access covered parking spaces.

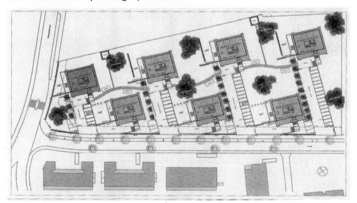

The use of galvanised steel for the external balconies and stairs is considered to be low maintenance and has a long life, thus reducing the embodied energy content. The wide balconies not only provide the owners with a large covered external space but also provide shade to the large windows in the summer. The external walls are constructed of a combination of large triple glazed elements and a lightweight infill construction of plasterboard, thermal insulation, cellulose comb made of corrugated paper with an external polypropylene sheet. The overall U value of this construction is better than the Swiss Minenergie standards. The comb material acts like a transparent insulation material, in that in winter it absorbs the low altitude solar radiation and thus increases the temperature which in effect acts like extra thermal insulation. In summer it is shielded from the sun by the large overhanging balcony.

Each flat has a mechanical ventilation system with heat recovery that not only gives a comfortable internal environment but also reduces the energy requirements as incidental heat gains (from people, lights, equipment and solar) can be effectively be reused.

These are some of the ways in which each floor can be subdivided. The access stairs and lift are drawn out from the façade, thus giving some degree of privacy to the occupiers of each floor.

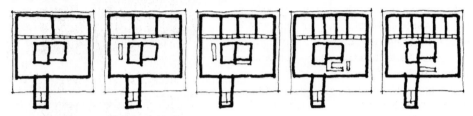

Environmental issues

Much of the construction was pre-made on site for final assembly.

Minimum use of wet trades.

The structural grid was selected to suit the dimensions of plasterboard.

Full use of part-finished and standard components.

Cranage was kept to a minimum.

Recycled materials or those with a high recycling capability were used throughout.

Low energy usage.

Timber columns.

Costs were 26% less than average costs for this size of development.

Design drivers
• Maximum use of environmentally building products.
• Optimum use of thermal insulation and glazing ratios to minimise heat losses.
• Use of locally sourced materials.
• Flexibility in planning room layouts to suit occupants' requirements.
• Improvement in environment quality of life.

Building type: Kindergarten in Stuttgart, Germany

Building size: 1390 m^2 (14 956 ft^2)
Client: Stuttgart City Authority
Architect: Joachim Eble Architektur, Tübingen
Main contractor: Schneck and Schaal, Tübingen
Service engineers: Schneck and Schaal, Tübingen
Timber contractor: Gaia Nouva with Holzbau Schûle, Boblingen
Photographs: Joachim Eble, Architektur
Client requirements: Low impact design with renewable energy and
the use of non-hazardous materials

Design details

The school, built for about 140 infant children,
forms part of the city's programme to develop
sustainable schools. The design is of a
compact form orientated towards the
southwest to maximise the availability of sun
and also enhances the local environment by
providing open spaces towards the streets.
The impact on the site is also minimised by this
plan form. During construction the impact on
the site was kept to a minimum by the use of
prefabricated structural elements.

The structure is solid timber prefabricated
panels made from locally sourced spruce.
The size of the panels was limited to 3 m
high by 9 m wide, as this was the
maximum size able to be transported to
the site.

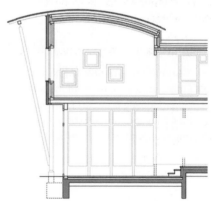

Finishes to the timber were based on natural materials, using linseed oil and mineral pigments in a solvent based on orange oil.

The large overhangs help to prevent the ingress of unwanted solar radiation and to some extent the deep reveals to the windows also help to reduce solar gains by providing further shading (although limited).

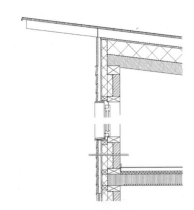

The *U* values of the structure are 25% below those set by regulations. It was estimated that the additional cost of doing this was paid back in energy savings in around 12 years, through an estimated 30% reduction in energy consumption.

Thermal insulation is provided by the thermal properties of the timber (100 mm thick), 160 mm of sprayed cellulose in the gap between the laminated panels and the 19 mm fibreboard behind the external cladding.

Hot water is provided by solar panels and a rainwater recovery system is also incorporated in the design.

U values
Walls: 0.2 W/m^{2}K
Windows: 2 W/m^{2}K
Roof: 0.2 W/m^{2}K
Floor: 0.15 W/m^{2}K

Cost: €1.93 million

Design drivers

- Low environmental impact and low impact materials.
- Use of locally sourced materials.
- Use of renewable energy.

Building type: Leonardo da Vinci Secondary School, Calais, France

Building size: 21 800 m^2 (234 568 ft^2)
Client: Nord Pas-de-Calais Regional Authority
Architect: Isabelle Colas and Fernand Soupey, Calais
Main contractor: Norpac and Thelu
Service engineers: Jacobs Serete, fluids, Berim
Environmental Consultants: François Septier, Nord Ingénière, Lille;
    Serge Sidoroff, Intakta, Paris
Client requirements: Low energy usage with significant input from
    renewable sources and environmental sustainability

Background

This school in northern France was designed to make use of
natural energy sources as well as the plentiful supply of water.
Environmental issues were positively encouraged in this design, from
the type of planting used to the materials used for construction. The
building uses natural light and ventilation as part of the low energy
strategy.

Design details

The buildings are grouped from the
southwest corner not only to maximise
the solar availability for both active
collection and passive use but also to
provide some degree of shelter from
the winds. The banking around the
east–west running dykes are planted
with willow, ash and alder along with
other indigenous plants which not only
enhance the environment but provide a
source of educational material.

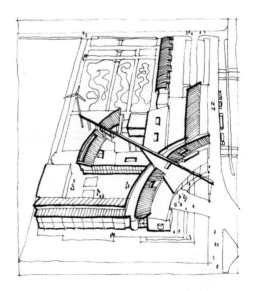

The water on site and also that collected from the roofs is used for both irrigation and flushing of toilets, thus reducing the demand for treated fresh water. Solar shading is provided by external shades and high-level windows allow daylight to penetrate into the interior.

This cross section demonstrates quite clearly the approach taken to ensure that daylight penetrates to the interior. This give a light airy feeling to the internal spaces as well as providing plenty of opportunity for cross ventilation.

   The structure is a concrete frame on a piled foundation (because of the high water table). The external walls are constructed of 110 mm fair faced blocks at lower level and ceramic cladding at high level. 50 mm of mineral wool insulation is placed between the external skin and the 190 mm insulating clay blocks which are painted on the internal face.

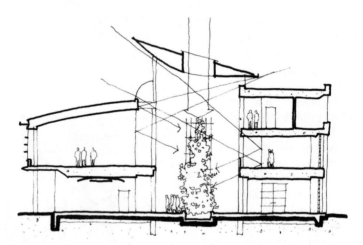

Environmental considerations played a significant role in the selection of materials for this building and many were analysed for embodied energy and life cycle considerations. Local raw materials were used where possible – Boulonnais sand and stone for the concrete, gabions from local stone and green roofs using locals plants were some of the areas benefiting from this analysis.

Energy issues played a very important part in the design of this school and it was the intention of the architects to make this school as autonomous as possible. The water runoff from the 3000 m^2 roof was channelled into a 200 m^3 pool and after filtration was used for used in the school for non-drinking requirements.

The heating system is rather complex as it relies on several sources of energy. High-efficiency gas-fired condensing boilers provide the bulk of the heating but a gas-fired co-generation plant (produces electricity and heat) supplements both the heating requirement and the electricity produced by a 135 kW wind generator.

The 75 m^2 photovoltaic panels provide low voltage electricity for the security system; the annual production is in the region of 5100 kWh. Hot water for the kitchens is provided by the 100 m^2 of solar collector tubes (Héliopac) on the roof over the kitchens. The heat from the panels is then passed through two 25 kW heat pumps which raises the temperature to 55°C. The water is stored in two 5000 litre tanks. In order to manage the various sources of energy a computer building energy management system is incorporated in the design.

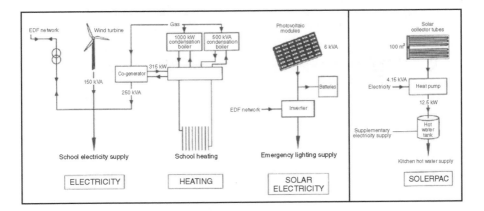

U values
Ground floor slab: 0.53 W/m^{2}K
Walls: 0.49 W/m^{2}K
Roof: 0.30 W/m^{2}K
Glazing: 1.94 W/m^{2}K

Energy consumption: 65.6 kWh/m^2/yr
(total gas usage)

The cost of the school was 8% more than the standards applied by the Region but the energy and water savings are 30%.

Design drivers

- Compact form giving good solar access and wind shelter.
- Use of internal spaces with top lighting to maximise natural light and ventilation.
- Integrated approach to environmental issues including a complex energy supply system.

Bibliography

The list has deliberately been kept to a minimum as there is so much literature on the subjects of Energy Efficiency and Environmental Design that to cover all of it would be overwhelming and not helpful in the context of this book.

Driving forces for reducing carbon emissions

Intergovernmental Panel on Climate Change
IPCC Secretariat
C/o World Meteorological Organization
7 bis Avenue de la Paix
C.P. 2300
CH-1211 Geneva 2
Switzerland
www.ipcc.ch/

'Our Energy Future – Creating a Low Carbon Economy', UK Government White Paper, 2003, HMSO

Environment

Rethinking Construction, *The Movement for Innovation*, Sustainability Working Group Report, 'Environmental Performance Indicators for Sustainable Construction', Published by the Centre for Sustainable Development, BRE, Watford.

The Green Building Bible, Green Building Press, PO Box 32, Llandysul SA44 5ZA, 2003

Environmental Issues in Construction – A review of issues and initiatives relevant to the building, construction and related industries, Vol 2 – Technical Review, CIRIA

Rough Guide to Sustainability, B Edwards and P Hyett, RIBA Publications, ISBN 1 85946 102 6

Useful sources of help on energy and environment

Building Research Establishment (BRE)
Garston
Watford WD2 7JR

Building Services Research and Information Association (BSRIA)
Old Bracknell Lane West
Bracknell
Berkshire RG12 7AH

Construction Industry Research and Information Association (CIRIA)
6 Story Gate
Westminster
London SW1P 3AU

Environment Agency
Rio House
Waterside Drive
Aztec West
Almondsbury
Bristol BS12 4UD

English Nature
Northminster House
Peterborough PE1 1AU

Highways Agency
St Christopher House
Southwark Street
London SE1 0TE

Scottish Environmental Protection Agency
Erskine Court
The Castle Business Park
Stirling FK9 4TR, Scotland

Chartered Institute of Building Services Engineers
222 Balham High Road
Balham
London SW12 9BS

Royal Institute of British Architects
99 Portland Place
London W1B 1AD

Royal Incorporation of Architects in Scotland
15 Rutland Square
Edinburgh EH1 2BE, Scotland

Web sites

Association for Environment Conscious Building: www.aecb.net/
Association for the Conservation of Energy: www.ukace.org/
BRE: www.bre.co.uk
BSRIA: www.bsria.co.uk
Centre for Alternative Technology: www.cat.org.uk/
Centre for Sustainable Energy: www.cse.org.uk/
CIRIA: www.ciria.org.uk
Construction Industry Council: www.cic.org.uk
Construction Products Association: www.cpa.org.uk
Department for Environment, Food and Rural Affairs (DEFRA):
     www.defra.gov.uk/
Department of Trade and Industry: www.dti.gov.uk/
English Nature: www.english-nature.org.uk
Environment Agency: www.environment-agency.gov.uk
Envirosearch: www.envirosearch.com
Forum for the Future: www.forumforthefuture.org.uk
National Green Specification from the Building Research Establishment:
     www.greenspec.co.uk
Office of the Deputy Prime Minister: www.odpm.gov.uk/
Solar Trade Association Ltd.: www.greenenergy.org.uk/sta/
Sustainable Aggregates Information Service: www.aggregain.org.uk
The Green Products database: www.newbuilder.co.uk

BCO Guide 2000, Best Practice in the specification of offices, British Council
     for Offices, 38 Lombard Street, London EC3V 8BS, ISBN 0 9524131 2 4

Building Regulations for England and Wales

Approved Document L1, *Conservation of fuel and power in dwellings*, 2002,
     The Stationery Office, PO Box 29, Norwich NR3 1GN, ISBN 0 11 753609 1

Approved Document L2, *Conservation of fuel and power in buildings other
     than dwellings*, 2002, The Stationery Office, PO Box 29, Norwich
     NR3 1GN, ISBN 0 11 753610 5

Approved Documents F1, F2, *Means of ventilation and condensation in roofs*,
     1995, The Stationery Office, PO Box 29, Norwich NR3 1GN,
     ISBN 0 11 752932 X

These can be obtained from the web address of the Office of the Deputy Prime Minister, www.odpm.gov.uk/

Building Regulations for Scotland

Scottish Executive Development Department
Victoria Quay
Edinburgh EH6 6QQ
www.scotland.gov.uk/build_regs/

Part K, *Ventilation of buildings*, available from http://www.scotland.gov.uk/library2/br/brk-01.asp

Building Regulations for Northern Ireland

Northern Ireland Office
Block B
Castle Buildings
Belfast BT4 3SG
Northern Ireland

Building Regulations for Ireland

Department of the Environment and Local Government
Custom House
Dublin 1
Ireland
http://www.environ.ie/doeihome.nsf?Open

Lighting and daylighting: Selected design guides from the Building Research Establishment

Legend
ECG – Energy Consumption Guide
GPG – Good Practice Guides
GPCS – Good Practice Case Studies
GIR – General Information Report

Lighting
Availability of daylight, DRG Hunt, BRE
Designing with innovative daylighting, PJ Littlefair, BRE, ISBN 1 86081 046 2

GPG 210 – Energy efficient lighting in the retail sector
GPG 223 – Cost-effective lighting for sports facilities: a guide for centre
managers and operators
GPG 245 – Desktop guide to daylighting
GIR 35 – Daylighting for sports halls – two case studies

Buildings

GPG 134 – Energy efficiency for shopping centres
GPG 211 – Drawing a winner: energy efficient design of sports centres
GPG 219 – Energy efficiency in swimming pools – for centre managers and
operators
GPG 304 – The purchaser's guide to energy-efficient buildings for industry
GPCS 361– Energy-efficient lighting for housing
GPCS 388 – Energy-efficient design of new industrial buildings
GPCS 391 – Energy-efficient refurbishment of industrial buildings
ECG 19 – Energy use in offices
GIR 53 – Building a sustainable future

General

GPG 237 – Natural ventilation in non-domestic buildings – a guide for
designers, developers and owners
GPG 290 – Ventilation and cooling option appraisal – a client's guide
GPG 291 – A designer's guide to the options for ventilating and cooling

Environmental design guide – for naturally ventilated and daylit offices, BRE,
ISBN 1 86081 227 9

Natural ventilation in non-domestic buildings, Applications Manual AM10:
1997, CIBSE

There is an extensive catalogue of design code information available from
CIBSE covering:
Commissioning
Lighting
Heating, cooling and air conditioning
Ventilation and air quality
Public Health Engineering
Energy, Sustainability and the Environment Controls
Electrical Services
Energy & Environmental Modelling
Lifts & Escalators
Fire Safety
Project Management

Facilities Management and Maintenance
Building Services

Environmental site layout planning: solar access, microclimate and passive cooling in urban areas, BRE, ISBN 1 86081 339 9

Designing buildings for daylight, J Bell and W Burt, BRE, ISBN 1 86081 026 8

Site layout planning for daylight and sunlight – a guide to good practice, P Littlefair, BRE, ISBN 0 85125 506 X

Museums' environment energy, M Cassar, Museums and Galleries Commission, HMSO, ISBN 0 11 290519 6

Handbook of sustainable building – an environmental preference method for selection of materials for use in construction and refurbishment, D Anink, C Boonstra and J Mak, James and James, 1998, ISBN 1 873936 38 9

Heat and light – a practical guide to energy conservation in church buildings, B Marks, St Andrew Press, 121 George Street, Edinburgh EH2 4YN, ISBN 0 86153 169 8

Make the most of it – a practical guide to energy conservation in churches, St Andrew Press, 121 George Street, Edinburgh EH2 4YN

Make even more of it, B Marks, Update on *Practical energy use in churches*, St Andrew Press, 121 George Street, Edinburgh EH2 4YN

AJ space for services, published by RIBA, 99 Portland Place, London W1B 1AD, ISBN 0 85139 171 0
(*an old publication but it still contains very relevant information*)

Displacement ventilation in non-industrial premises – guidebook 1, H Skistad, REHVA, Ravenstein 3, B-1000 Brussels, 2002

Environment, energy and economy – strategies for sustainability, Y Kaya and K Yokobori, United Nations University Press, ISBN 92 808 0911 3

Saline Ostia Antica, F Sartogo, Ecology in Architecture 2, Alinea Publishing Company, Firenze, 1999, ISBN 88 8125 257 0

TN11/95 *Control of natural ventilation*, BSRIA, Old Bracknell Lane West, Bracknell RG12 7AH

Thermie Programme Action publications:
Energy efficient lighting in industrial buildings
Energy efficient lighting in schools
Energy efficient lighting in offices
Published by Building Research Establishment, Garston, Watford, WD2 7JR

A guide to the energy efficiency design of school buildings, DfES publications, PO Box 5050, Sherwood Park, Annesley, NG15 0DJ

Energy in architecture – the European passive solar handbook, Batsford, ISBN 0 7134 69188

Building for energy efficiency – the client's briefing guide, Construction Industry Council, 26 Store Street, London WC1E 7BT, ISBN 1 89867 09 5

Principles of hybrid ventilation, ed. P Heiselberg, ECBCS Support Services Unit, c/o Faber Maunsell Ltd., Beaufort House, 94–96 Newhall Street, Birmingham B3 1PB, 2002

Acoustics

A guide to the energy efficiency design of educational buildings, Building Handbook, DfES, download from www.dfee.gov.uk/schblds/

Applied acoustics, G Porges, Edward Arnold, 1977, ISBN 0 71 312659 0

Building Bulletin 93, acoustic design of schools, HMSO, 2001

Design standards for the sound insulation of music practice rooms, J Miller, Acoustics Bulletin of the Institute of Acoustics, Vol 18, No 6, Nov/Dec 1993, pp 54–58

Detailing for acoustics, D Templeton and P Lord, 3rd edition, E&FN Spon, London 1996, ISBN 0 419 20210 2

Noise control in buildings, a practical guide for architects and engineers, C M Harris, McGraw-Hill, 1994, ISBN 0 07 026887 8

Noise control in building services, A Fry, Sound Research Laboratories Ltd. Pergamon Press, Oxford, 1998, ISBN 0 08 034067 9

Sound control for homes, BRE and CIRIA, BRE 238, CIRIA Report 127, 1993, ISBN 085125 55900

Index

very low energy office building 101
visual comfort 40–3
visual confusion 43, 44

wallcoverings, plastic bottles 256
walls
    external 86
    heat transfer 77
    noise reduction 49
    Trombe walls 92, 93–4
wards, hospital 140
warm periods
    thermal mass 91
    see also summer
washing machine doors 241
waste minimisation 201, 207–8
water
    consumption reduction 199
    environmental self assessment 210
    grey 241, 273
    ground water 198
    issues 220
    purification space 174
    rainwater 199, 250, 269
    storage of cold 174
    sustainability 198–9
water features 199, 234
watersheds 198, 199
White Paper on Energy 7, 8–9

wind
    effects 149–51
    generators 238, 242, 273
    industrial units 253–4
    shelter 56–8, 149–50
    site planning 197
    turbines 237
    turbulence 150–1
windows
    daylight 16, 58–69
    deep plan form 15, 54–5
    natural ventilation 16–17, 67–9
    noise reduction 49
    openings 67, 68, 109–11
    overhangs 64, 269
    solar protection 16
    thermal performance 58–69
winter
    natural ventilation calculations 111
    office temperatures 12
    thermal mass 90–1, 93
    ventilation issues 115–17
    see also cool periods
Wirksworth private house 229–30, 249–51
wood burning stoves 230
work opportunities 208–9
worship, lighting places of 141–2

Zürich balance concepts 231